CW00821419

Archaeopteryx, the Primordial Bird

A Case of Fossil Forgery

Archaeopteryx, the Primordial Bird

A Case of Fossil Forgery

Fred Hoyle
& Chandra Wickramasinghe

Photographs by R. S. Watkins

Christopher Davies

Published by
Christopher Davies (Publishers) Ltd.
P.O. Box 403, Sketty,
Swansea, SA2 9BE.

ISBN 0 7154 0665 5

Set in Garamond by
Dynevor Printing Company
Llandybïe, Dyfed, Wales.
Printed by
Jolly & Barber Ltd.
Rugby, Warwickshire.
Bound by
Butler & Tanner Ltd.
Frome, Somerset.

Contents

Preface

Archaeopteryx, 'ancient winged creature', was supposedly discovered in the limestone rocks of southern Bavaria, rocks that are about 160 million years old. *Archaeopteryx* has an undoubtedly genuine component to it, a bony skeleton scarcely distinguishable, if at all, from the reptilian dinosaur *Compsognathus*, 'pretty jaw'. *Archaeopteryx* differs from *Compsognathus*, however, in possessing an extensive coating of feathers, feathers whose impressions in the rock are remarkably perfect in a specimen supposedly discovered in the year 1861, and quite perfect in a specimen supposedly discovered in 1877. An almost perfect imprint of a single feather about three inches long had appeared already in 1860-61, a feather wholly modern in its aerodynamical characteristics. Since the skeletal features of *Archaeopteryx* are not at all suited to flight — the creature had no proper anchorage for its tail feathers and no breast muscles to speak of wherewith to beat its wings — it challenges credulity to imagine that the flight feathers could be such as would permit the complex aerobatic feats of modern birds. A forger of the feathers, on the other hand, would have had no option but to use modern feathers for his dubious work.

The major claimed discoveries of 1861 and 1877 were associated with the same family, and in particular with Dr. Karl Häberlein, the medical officer of the district in which the finds were supposedly made, a person about whom the distinguished German paleontologist, Andreas Wagner, expressed reservations. Wagner was the discoverer of *Compsognathus*, the genuine part of the *Archaeopteryx* fossil, and he more than anyone else would have been in a position to comment with authority on the genuineness or otherwise of the feathery adornments of *Archaeopteryx*. It is unfortunate therefore that Wagner died immediately after the appearance of the 1861 specimen, died unexpectedly it is said.

The 1861 specimen was sold to the British Museum for what at that time was an unprecedentedly large sum for a fossil, while the specimen of 1877 was sold to a Herr Vogler in Frankfurt for 36,000 gold marks. The 1877 specimen was subsequently acquired by the Museum für Naturkunde in Berlin.

Some opponents of our views have sought to weaken the circumstantial implications of these facts by stating that three further feather-bearing specimens of *Archaeopteryx* have also appeared in one way or another, the Teyler Museum specimen originally found in 1855, the Eichstätt specimen of 1951, and the poorly preserved Maxberg specimen of 1956. The inference we are intended to draw is that the existence of these further revelations exonerate the specimens of 1860-61 and 1877. But this polemic is yet another fraud, for the three further specimens do not possess unmistakable impressions of feather barbs. They merely possess indefinite markings, as does almost any piece of rock, that persons of inadequate near vision can interpret to suit themselves.

The question of the authenticity of *Archaeopteryx* was first raised by Dr. Lee M. Spetner, who was a collaborator in the photographic investigations described in this book. Where we have eventually differed from others of our collaborators is in the motivations we attribute to the frauds of 1860-61 and 1877. At first sight it seemed as if a Darwinist plot might be lying there, waiting to be unearthed. Although others may still feel this to be so, we were led by our search of the literature to a different conclusion, which we describe in the later chapters of the book. Ironically, a Darwinist bias does indeed exist today, in the modern attempts to defend the fossil.

An attempt to defend *Archaeopteryx* appeared very recently in the magazine *Science* (issue for 2 May, 1986, pp. 622-626, by A. J. Charig, F. Greenaway, A. C. Milner, C. A. Walker and P. J. Whybrow). The case offered for the defence rests mainly on two points. It is said that matching hairline cracks are to be found on both the main slab and counterslab of the fossil, with the implication that because some of the supposed cracks traverse feather-bearing areas the feather impressions must be genuine. These supposed cracks are the lines or edges discussed in Chapter 4, and which are to be seen there in Plate XVI. Because of differences of colorations on the two sides of the lines of Plate XVI, we were led to interpret the lines as edges of one or more overlying layers rather than as cracks. Plate XVI is reproduced, it may be noted, without any touching up by us, directly from the print supplied by the commercial company that processed our film, as indeed were all the Plates in this book. The low resolution pictures appearing in *Science*, on the other hand, could not possibly in our opinion show such fine details as a hairline crack unless they were artificially enhanced, as for example by the use of a mapping pen.

The claimed matching hairline crack, marked p-p in Figure 2A of Charig *et al*, crosses a region that was excavated by the Museum itself at some time between 1862 and 1895, a process that would — if the fossil were genuine — have involved a good deal of hammer and chisel work. To base claims on what one has altered oneself is in our scheme of things a dubious procedure, and to do so without informing one's readers that alterations have been made is, again in our view, an even more dubious procedure.

The second argument of Charig *et al* is that dendritic patterns (treelike growths of dark inorganic crystals) match closely on the slab and counterslab, even though some of the patterns occur in the feathered regions. Why the group of Museum staff members chose to make such a demonstrably incorrect statement is unclear to us. Plate XIX shows with overwhelming force that dendritic patterns do not match between an extensive area of the upper right wing of the main slab and the corresponding area of the counterslab. Not only this, but missing tree-like growths on the main slab have been artificially covered over by a layer of feather-bearing material. On good quality magnifications as in Plate XX they can even be seen peeping faintly through from below. Instead of considering the major example given in Plates XIX and XX, Charig *et al* choose a minor example, minor because the area displayed carries only a small region of feather-bearing material. Yet in our photographs even this very small feather-bearing region is just the same as the major region of Plate XIX, the dendritic patterns disappear, the patterns being largely hidden as in Plate XX by a feather-bearing layer of some artificial material. This attempt to claim the opposite of what is easily visible to the eye suggests that, with the Museum's authority behind them, the authors of the *Science* article take the view that anything goes. The danger inherent in this attitude is that, all too easily, the Museum may find from now on that nothing goes.

20 May, 1986   *Fred Hoyle*
                                Chandra Wickramasinghe

Acknowledgement

We are grateful to Shirwan Al-Mufti, Robert Rabilizirov, Lee Spetner and John Watkins in various stages of the work for their valuable assistance.

CHAPTER 1

The Origin of Birds

A bird that often passes almost unnoticed attracts the attention of a particular household, because it chooses to nest in a creeper two yards from the front door, which is not the best possible spot one might think, since the female flies off the nest in apparent alarm whenever anyone comes to the house or comes out of it. Yet a bird of this species, the spotted flycatcher, is there year after year in the same spot, a spot so unusual for a normally unobstrusive bird that one must suppose a memory of this precise place has become established in a family of birds, with the knowledge passing generation to generation from parents to offspring.

The spotted flycatcher winters in tropical and southern Africa, setting an amazing problem, for how can a little creature without complex electronics to aid it such as man would use, a creature with a brain inside a head only about an inch in diameter, find its way from Africa to Britain, to a region of Britain, to a valley in that region, and at last to a creeper beside the front door of a particular household? The word 'birdbrain' used by humans in a derogatory sense about each other scarcely seems justified. Indeed one can only wonder if birds use the term 'humanbrain' when they chirrup in a derogatory sense about each other.

'Birders' is the noun used by Americans for people who have developed a passion for bird watching. Identifying birds by name is the motivation it seems of most bird-watchers. We ourselves, we must admit, have never derived much satisfaction from naming things. Rather the interest lies for us in watching what birds do and in asking why and how they do it. Distinguishing the willow warbler from the chiffchaff is a subtle affair beyond our ability. What we do notice, however, is that these birds collectively have a species liking for clusters of half-grown deciduous trees, especially those with a profusion of small leaves, trees such as the birch. When the young appear in early summer you can see why, for the tiny young birds, only two or three inches long, practise flying by short forays from bough to bough, safely hidden by the foliage from predators on the outside. This apparently simple flitting from bough to bough conceals a tricky aerodynamic problem. When a bird lands on a bough it does not crash into it, as we would do if we were to fall down a tree. First, the bird goes at considerable speed towards its chosen landing spot. Then at the very last moment it checks speed. It effectively stops and falls lightly onto the chosen place, a manoeuvre that is effected by using what in aeronautics is called the stalling speed. Early airplanes had only a small margin of safety between available flight speeds and stalling speeds, so that take-offs and landings were always a chancey business requiring much skill from human pilots if accidents were to be avoided. Birds on the other hand, even young birds only a week out of the nest, learn the much greater skill of controlling stalling speeds so delicately as to be able to land gently as they will, with stalling speeds of utility value to them, not a danger. It is the flight feathers of birds which make the big difference, because feathers have far superior aerodynamic properties to any airplane wing yet designed by man. Travellers by plane will have noticed how the wings are broken into a more complex shape during the moments just before landing. This more complex shape gives to the plane wing something of the properties of a feather, but only rather crudely.

It is easy to tell from the sustained low volume twitterings of many birds when an owl has landed nearby. During the daytime the owl will be looking for a quiet sheltered spot where it can sleep. The twitterings aren't so much a danger signal as a design to stop the owl from sleeping. If you watch what goes on, you will sometimes see two or three of the bolder spirits go right in and perch immediately beside the owl and twitter directly into his or her ear. It is to stop this from happening that the owl looks so carefully for a sheltered spot where it is awkward for the bolder spirits to come very close. Otherwise they will give the owl hell and pretty soon he or she will feel obliged to leave, to the satisfaction of the rest of the community. Whether in such a case the bolder spirits receive any form of social reward from the community, a distinction for gallantry as it were, is a more difficult question to answer.

Other examples of gallantry are not hard to find. When a hawk is up, the twittering of the community becomes loud and sustained. It is a real warning signal now. Two old crows take-off and climb laboriously up into the sky. Once on a level with the hawk they make straight for it, boring in on the invader from either side. But of course the hawk avoids them easily by a mere shake of its powerful wings. The crows try again and again, without getting anywhere near the hawk, so for a while you think the defence of the community offered by the crows to be hopeless. But amazingly the hawk eventually veers away and disappears. What has happened is that all those little shakes by which the hawk avoided the crows has thrown off its visual analysis of small objects near the ground, thrown off sufficiently to make an accurate dive onto prey hardly impossible. So the hawk goes elsewhere, riding the air currents instead of continuing to use-up valuable energy in hovering, and the crows sink back to the ground, exhausted, whether or not to receive the plaudits of the community. When a human commits an act of bravery, 'beyond the call of duty' as the citation for the Victoria Cross puts it, we attach the highest virtue to the situation. When an animal commits an act of bravery we refuse to accept that the situation could ever be 'beyond the call of duty', attributing it to 'mere instinct' which the animal has no option but to obey. But whether there is really any difference is a good question, a good question for the Moral Sciences Tripos at Cambridge, if ever the Moral Sciences Tripos got around to asking anything so sensible.

It is interesting to observe the circumstances in which birds quarrel and in which they don't, because once again the situation has a relation to human politics, morals and philosophy. Birds quarrel most furiously within their own varieties. They quarrel when different species happen to have similar preferences for habitat and for food. But they quarrel not at all with others of radically different abilities and habits. When the really powerful flying birds, the martins, swallows and swifts arrive in the spring, the indigenous community doesn't appear to notice them at all. The powerful flyers form their own community without noticable interaction with the local community.

The spotted flycatcher forms an interesting comparison with the swallows. Both are migratory between Europe and Africa, both are insect-catching. Yet their shapes and abilities are markedly different, so different as to make one wonder how two generally similar modes of life could be achieved so disparately. The answer lies partly in the strength of Earth's gravity and in the density of the atmosphere, which inevitably produce a clash between flying and landing. Optimum flight demands long feathers as in the swallow and swift, but long feathers make landing and take-off difficult, in the case of the swift almost impossible. This creates two distinct niches, one for birds that fly almost perpetually, the other for those who develop specialist tricks on the ground. A specialist trick of the flycatcher is to remove the stings of wasps and bees before swallowing them, which the powerfully flying birds cannot do.

All insect-eating birds prefer big stuff, blow flies and horseflies, which of course is excellent from a human point of view. Unfortunately, however, none of them will touch small stuff like midges and black fly, so long the larger more nutritive insects are available. This whole matter deserves as serious a study as the quark model of fundamental particles, because what humans need more than they need most things is a tiny bird an inch to an inch-and-a-half long with a passion for midge and black fly, which birds, existing in vast numbers, could make living in the northern latitudes of the Earth reasonably tolerable in summer time.

Living in the same valley as the spotted flycatcher which nested only two yards from the front door of one of the houses was a carrion crow called Hitchcock that went clean off its rocker. The thing started one can only suppose by Hitchcock pecking at window panes for insects. Then Hitchcock caught sight of his reflection in the glass and disliked what he saw, as many humans have done before him. Being a brave crow, Hitchcock stood his ground and gave the window pane all he'd got. So long as the assaults occurred only on occasions when Hitchcock simply chanced to glance in a window pane, the affair remained within bounds. The situation became more serious, however, when Hitchcock decided the whole valley had been invaded by enemy aliens who were invariably to be found sheltering behind sheets of glass. Thereafter he began deliberately to seek out sheets of glass wherever they could be found. It was also noticed that the more Hitchcock delivered his assaults the better he became at it. You would be wakened at five o'clock on a May morning by Hitchcock delivering on the bedroom window an attack sounding just like closeby machine-gun fire. Nobody throughout the valley dared to sleep with their bedroom windows open even in the hottest weather, which explained how the bird came to be called Hitchcock.

As practise made still more perfect, Hitchcock took to attacking the windscreens of cars. A visitors' car would arrive at a fine viewpoint at the valley head, likely enough an elderly couple enjoying a well-earned holiday. While still seated in the car they would start drinking their morning coffee or unpacking lunch. Pretty soon there would be a commotion of big black wings and Hitchcock would settle himself down on the bonnet of the car, cleverly using the stalling speed trick. The occupants would usually have a moment of grace trying to recover from the shock and from the hot coffee which had been spilt, then would come the frenzied attack. You could watch it all safely from a distance, knowing exactly what was going to happen. In the distance you could hear the car engine come to life, you could hear it revving furiously. A fleeting instant later the car would leap convulsively into motion, its owners desperately intent on reaching some other delectable spot from which to continue their well-earned holiday.

Towards the end of summer there comes the week or so in early September when the martins and swallows perch in long rows on telephone wires, and there are all sorts of problems and questions you can ask yourself about this practice. It has the obvious aspect of a roll call, taken immediately in advance of the immense migratory flight to the south. But there seems to be more to it than that. The birds choose different wires at different times of day, and one can ask whether the choices are being made with respect to the direction of the sun. Pairs of birds keep breaking out of the line. Each pair wheels and jinks together in unison in a complex path before returning to the wire. Is this row of birds on the wire really a prospective flight formation you can wonder, with inexperienced birds placed between experienced ones, and with them learning who their neighbours are going to be?

The visual acuity of birds is another thing to be considered. Throw away a few scraps of food within a mile of almost any coast and within a minute or two you are likely to have gulls landing there and snatching up the food. Throw away bits of paper of superficially the same appearance on the ground and the gulls won't come, although an odd gull may wheel past for a moment and then go contemptuously away. Angle for angle this performance by the gull is comparable optically to a man-made surveillance satellite, showing by practical demonstration that the eyes of birds must possess all the refined corrections for aberrations, coma and astigmatism of the best man-made optical systems. How this came about is supposedly explained in biology by the theory of evolution through natural selection. The logic of this theory is the following. In a fixed environment, natural selection operates in a species to prevent adaptation to the environment from becoming worse, because defective individuals are selected against in the competition for survival. Most critics of the theory have been inclined to accept this statement as plausible, although it is easy to see that if strict mathematical standards were adopted the logic would have to be rejected even at this first gambit. Humans have lost the ability to synthesise vitamins, which is an example of a disadaptation to the environment having occurred. The loss of fur was very likely an initial disadaptation also, as Alfred Russel Wallace pointed out more than a century ago. But let us accept the opening gambit and see how the game then goes.

If steps backward are excluded, then the only steps which can be made must be forwards. But will any steps at all be made one can ask? The answer must be yes, because no material system can be copied a very large number of times without occasional miscopying occurring. Overwhelmingly, most miscopyings will be steps backward, but with steps backwards excluded, the steps are restricted to the occasional forward ones. So where does this leave us? Nowhere at all really. There is nothing in the logic to tell us whether the steps forward will be sufficient in number and in kind to produce the superb optical system of a gull's eye. So what has been done for over a century and a quarter, with each generation imprinting a mental pattern on the next generation, is to quit logic by an appeal to belief. Since the gull's eye exists it must be so, the claim is made, a claim so weak in logic that it has no value worth speaking about. If you had been born with a fortune and had spent it improvidently you would have little money now in your bank account. You have indeed little money in your account. Therefore you were born with a fortune and have spent it improvidently. The mental process here is just the same as it is in biology. Such inferential conclusions are empty, however, unless it can be proved strictly that the conclusion could be arrived at in no other way, as for instance in the example it would be necessary to prove that only by being born with a fortune and subsequently spending it could one arrive at a small bank account. In biology it has never been proved that the optical system of a gull's eye can be arrived at in no other way except through evolution by natural selection, and in the absence of such an essential proof what is done is to replace proof by an article of faith without which no biologist could secure a job.

It may at least be said for 19th century biology that it eschewed miracles. It did not claim that an eyeless creature could suddenly become endowed with the superbly compensated gull's eye, all in a moment as a result of only one or two mistakes of copying. The argument was that there had to be a vast number of small steps, with each step forward only a tiny improvement on the preceding state of affairs. Strangely enough this view persisted for nearly a century before it was seen to contain an almost obvious mathematical error. The critical point is that every definitive step, every step no matter how small, requires the previous form of creature to become extinct as a consequence of not possessing the slight improvement in question. That is to say, the slight improvement is bought at a cost in deaths that can be shown to be large for every step that is made. And if there are many steps — as the 19th century biologists supposed — the cost is easily seen to become impossibly heavy. Since the straightforward disproof of the standard theory of evolution through nature selection was discovered a generation ago attempts have repeatedly been made to save the oldtime theory by just the kind of multiplicity of invented hypotheses which Ockham's razor warns us to avoid. To no avail, since attempts to change the selective model has only had the effect of replacing one form of disproof by another. The situation is quite clear. The gull's eye, and indeed a multitude of other remarkable abilities possessed by plants and animals, cannot have evolved by many small steps, because the cost in lives lost would be impossibly heavy to bear.

Two alternatives remain, evolution in a comparatively few large steps essentially miraculous in their origin, or evolution in large steps due to an importation onto the Earth of genetic systems from outside the Earth. Quite apart from the aversion of the scientist to miracles, there are plenty of reasons why importations from outside provide the correct explanation for the evolution of life on the Earth. Returning to the case of the eye, while the gull's eye is so near to optical perfection the eyes possessed by terrestial creatures are generally very far indeed from performing optimally with respect to the light intensity. Full sunlight, defined shall we say by the glare of a tropical snowfield, is far too bright. Dark glasses are obligatory in such conditions. Dark glasses are advisable in any tropical light, even after the light has been reflected poorly with only, say, 10 percent efficiency by the land surface. The most comfortable light intensity for the human eye lies in the range from one hundredth to one thousandth of full sunlight, which is about the intensity of the artificial lighting used in a draftsman's office. This is roughly the intensity that would be seen by a person standing on a snowfield on one of the satellites of the planet Uranus, which makes you think a bit. Photosynthesis by plants also works with poor efficiency in full sunlight. Photosynthesis works with maximum efficiency at significantly lower intensities. Indeed if the question be asked down to what intensity of light can plants grow, the answer is, interestingly, down to about the level the human eye feels most comfortable. The natural thought is that, since the eye is so perfectly constructed from the standpoint of physical optics, it is probably also well-constructed from the point of view of the intensity of the light in the environment in which it evolved, which places the environment in the outer regions of the solar system, or in some other environment of similar light intensity, with the same being true for the complex biochemical processes of photosynthesis.

Some biologists have asked what is to be gained by such a theory, and the answers to this question are several. First, it corresponds better to the facts. Second, the Universe at large is much better fitted to bear the genetic cost of evolution than the Earth alone. And third, most problems of origin turn out to broaden in their horizons until they become cosmological in scope, so it is likely the problem of life, perhaps the biggest of all problems, is universal in its scale. Scientists often seem to feel that a simple theory is more likely to be correct than a complex one. While simplicity, once we understand the relevant mathematics, does seem to be a property of the basic physical laws, complexity is the hallmark of the applications of those laws. A river flows smoothly in a broad gently-shelving bed and it all looks placid and simple, but let the bed of the river fall suddenly by a hundred feet and amazing complexities are instantly let loose at the resulting waterfall. What had been the fairly simple problem of describing the smooth flow of water suddenly becomes essentially insoluble in its details at the drop in the bed of the river. Surely this is the way it goes in all aspects of the universe, probably with the most significant occurrences taking place in hiatuses, in disasters, in sudden shifts from smooth uneventful conditions. The same appears to be generally true of human society, with governments perpetually trying to maintain conditions of smooth flow, but with the events that really determine history occurring in uncontrolled shifts, as society plunges in its evolution over a series of waterfalls which set all manner of unexpected events in train.

In our view so it has been for the development of life on

the Earth. From time to time the Earth has been flooded by immense genetic storms which changed many species drastically and sometimes even extinguished them altogether. The view we have maintained since 1978 is that viruses provide the vehicle of biological change, not the ineffective miscopying from generation to generation of the usual evolutionary theory. Viruses have the ability to enter cells, and having entered they disrupt and change the processes occurring therein. Often the disruptions lead to the disturbances we call disease, which, if serious enough, can produce the death of a plant or animal. In other cases, however, the disruptions are sufficient to change the invaded organism, sometimes mildly, sometimes appreciably, without the changes being terminal. Viruses can add whole new genes not possessed previously by an organism, and very likely they can promote radical reorganisations of the whole of the genetic material within the cells of an organism.

Evolution by viral invasion solves problems that appear insuperable for the 19th century theory. According to standard theory, mammals evolved from a reptilian branch called synapsida. But the genetic material of a mammal is grossly different from that of a reptile. It is different in amount and it is quite different in its organisation. To pass from the one to the other would entail steps in which organisational structure was changed, as for instance whole chromosomes being changed. This sets the problem for species which propagate by sexual reproduction that a changed individual cannot mate successfully unless a member of the opposite sex can be found possessing almost exactly the same change. It is not sufficient to postulate an amazing feat of miscopying that contrived to produce a highly beneficial structural change. We have to postulate the simultaneous occurrence of three miracles. Whatever miracle occurs to a male, say, there must be the even greater miracle that just the same structural change occurs by a chance miscopying to a female, and furthermore the two miracles must happen in the same place at much the same time, otherwise the changed male will not find the changed female. Mathematically, this means the probability of any appreciable change being successfully propagated is the product of three small numbers, making the result negligibly small.

The only suggestion we have heard for overcoming this impasse in the standard theory is to suppose the changed male and the changed female are identical twins derived from the same miscopied sex cells of their parents. On this supposition one would have to suppose, additionally, that every one of the major genetic changes needed to go from a reptile to a mammal took place through a single pair of identical twins, whose incestuous offspring then replaced the whole of their species. Since the rest of the members would not die voluntarily, the requirement is for them to be exterminated by the incestuous progeny, a process that has to happen very many times, with the ancestral line of every species we see around us today being narrowed down to just a single pair on thousands of occasions in the past, a proposition that textbooks on the standard theory are careful not to mention, so exceedingly unlikely is it. Such frequent exterminations are simply another way of stating the evolutionary cost argument already discussed above.

Evolution by viral addition avoids this devastating difficulty, because males and females can be similarly changed by the same externally-imposed virus, and also with the possibility that the virus could be infectious from one individual to another, thereby changing simultaneously a considerable fraction of all the members of a species. The argument is so cogent that it is beginning to achieve currency in some biological circles, but only on the doubtful basis that the viruses in question are indigenous to the Earth, which leaves unsolved the crucial problem of the origin of the viruses in the first place. At first sight it might seem attractive to suppose the required viruses have evolved within micro-organisms, for example within bacteria. Bacteria exist in enormous numbers — there are about a hundred million of them to a typical gram of garden soil. So the amount of copying of genetic material that goes on in bacteria is correspondingly enormous, permitting even unlikely genetic changes to arise one might seek to argue. The trouble, however, is that viruses of the kind that enter and leave the cells of bacteria do not, so far as is known, interact with the more complex cells of higher plants and animals. Nor could the genes which produce the optical perfection of a gull's eye evolve in bacteria one might think, since of course bacteria do not have eyes. There are many such arguments to show the idea does not work, and that it should be considered at all demonstrates how hard-pressed even non-standard biological thinking has become.

The only sensible line is to regard evolutionary viruses as being incident on the Earth from outside, with the implication that the genes responsible for a gull's eye evolved elsewhere, in other creatures with eyes. But why not? The universe is after all a big place. Viral invasions are happening in some degree all the time. Invasion happens in a minor degree with almost every cough and cold we contract. It happens more seriously in world-wide attacks like the influenza epedemic of 1918, and it happens still more seriously every few centuries in the large scale attack of some hitherto unknown disease. Yet even the worst diseases of recorded history are very likely only modest affairs compared to what happens in a real

relative duration of eras	era	period	epoch	duration in million of years (approx.)	millions of years ago (approx.)
Cenozoic		Quaternary	Holocene	approx. last 10,000 years	
Mesozoic			Pleistocene	2.5	2.5
	Cenozoic		Pliocene	4.5	7
Paleozoic		Tertiary	Miocene	19	26
			Oligocene	12	38
			Eocene	16	54
			Paleocene	11	65
	Mesozoic	Cretaceous		71	136
		Jurassic		54	190
		Triassic		35	225
		Permian		55	280
Precambrian		Carboniferous — Pennsylvanian		45	325
		Carboniferous — Mississippian		20	345
	Paleozoic	Devonian		50	395
		Silurian		35	430
		Ordovician		70	500
		Cambrian		70	570
		Precambrian		4,030	

formation of Earth's crust 4,600,000,000 years ago

Figure 1: Geological epochs and their durations.

genetic storm. Big genetic storms are so severe that they produce extinctions of whole species. The worst genetic storm of all seems to have occurred about 65 million years ago, when every species of animal weighing more than 50 pounds became extinct, including the famous extinction of the large dinosaurs. The dinosaurs were far from being alone in their fate, which was shared by nearly half the genera of all animals. None of the many proposed physical and chemical causes of these disasters appear to us to be plausible, for the reason that, while abiological disasters could conceivably attenuate a species, wholly exterminating a species is unlikely. Physical extermination is very difficult, as is evidenced by the inability of man, with all his technology, to exterminate scarcely a single one among the many millions of insect species. The extinctions of 65 million years ago were not confined to large animals. They went all the way down from the largest animals even to small micro-organisms, and they occurred in every kind of habitat, including the bottom of the sea, showing that whatever the cause was, it drenched the whole Earth, reaching into every nook and cranny.

It will be useful for future reference to set out the geological periods and time scales of relevance to the evolutionary development of terrestrial life, as shown in Figure 1. (From *Ency. Britt.*, Vol. 7, 1066). The time of 65 million years ago will be seen to lie near the boundary between the Cretaceous period and the Tertiary, the latter with its subdivisions of Paleocene, Eocene, Oligocene, Miocene and Pliocene.

Figure 2 shows the record of the beginnings and endings of a number of genera of small sea-living animals, their periods of existence from the beginning of the Cretaceous onwards being shown by the solid bars. Plankton are surface creatures and the benthic creatures are (or were) from large oceanic depths.

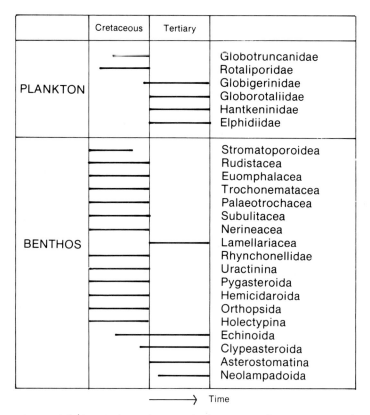

	Cretaceous	Tertiary	
PLANKTON			Globotruncanidae Rotaliporidae Globigerinidae Globorotaliidae Hantkeninidae Elphidiidae
BENTHOS			Stromatoporoidea Rudistacea Euomphalacea Trochonematacea Palaeotrochacea Subulitacea Nerineacea Lamellariacea Rhynchonellidae Uractinina Pygasteroida Hemicidaroida Orthopsida Holectypina Echinoida Clypeasteroida Asterostomatina Neolampadoida

⟶ Time

Figure 2: The bars indicate the periods of existence of various genera of small sea-living animals, with plankton from the surface water and benthic creatures from considerable oceanic depths (After D. A. Russell in *Syllogeus* No. 12, National Museums of Canada, 1976).

Of the 15 cases of extinction, 14 terminate at the Cretaceous-Tertiary boundary, which is to say about 65 million years ago. Of the 9 cases which began in post-Jurassic times, 5 started at the Cretaceous-Tertiary boundary, suggesting that the situation 65 million years ago could be a beginning as well as an ending, as one might expect for an immense genetic storm.

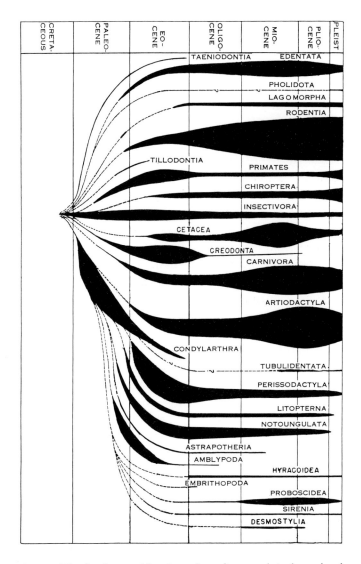

Figure 3: The fossil record for the orders of mammals is shown by the solid areas, the dotted continuations being only conjectural. The widths of the solid strips indicate changing numbers of species in the various orders.

The solid areas of Figure 3 show the fossil record for the orders of mammals, with the dotted extensions drawn to correspond to the way evolution is supposed to have occurred according to the standard theory. The striking aspects of Figure 3 are, first that no detailed connections have been found between the orders, and second that the conjectured connections converge to a common origin close to the Cretaceous-Tertiary boundary, again suggesting that the Cretaceous-Tertiary boundary was a beginning as well as an ending. It was the product of an immense genetic storm that wiped-out some creatures and drastically changed others, with the present mammalian orders emerging as grafts onto previously-existing stock. According to this view there is no requirement for all the mammals to have emerged from a single graft. There could have been several or many grafts, with the various mammalian orders always being separated, thereby explaining neatly why connections between the orders have not been found.

It is hardly an objection to this theory that evidence, often fragmentary, of mammalian characteristics dating from before the Cretaceous-Tertiary boundary have been found, since evolution by sudden grafting will always produce evident similarities between the situations as they existed before and after the grafting, especially where the gross features of the skeleton of a creature are concerned. In short, connecting what existed before with what came after a big discontinuity is an uncertain process.

Turning at last to the origin of birds, we naturally ask if birds could also be the product of a sudden grafting onto reptilian stock, with the possibility that the grafting process also took place at the Crectaceous-Tertiary boundary? Paleontologists almost to the man or woman would argue not, because there is believed to be a considerable body of evidence to show that birds existed already in the later part of the Cretaceous period. Much of the evidence is skeletal and fragmentary however, so that for the reason just given it can, with a few exceptions only, be discounted. The exceptions are for cases where fossils of whole creatures have been recovered.

The exceptions go by the names *Hesperornis* together with the similar *Baptornis, Ichthyornis* and the similar *Apatornis,* all these from the later Cretaceous, and the famous (or infamous according as one sees it) *Archaeopteryx* from the middle of the Jurassic period, about 160 million years ago. *Archaeopteryx* is a creature supposedly with essentially modern feathers, perfectly adapted for flying, but without either the muscles or attachments to use the feathers for flight. So here is an absurd situation to start with.

From the time of its supposed discovery in 1861 until well into the present century *Archaeopteryx* was believed to be a bird that still retained reptilian features in its skeleton. As time went on, however, the emphasis shifted to *Archaeopteryx* being a gliding reptile with some bird-like features, as well as the feathers of course. By 1954 when de Beer's supposedly definitive book on the subject appeared (G. de Beer, British Museum, Natural History Publication) the number of birdlike features present in the skeleton had retreated to only four, however. By 1979 they had retreated to one, the so-called furcula or wishbone, and it is now our understanding that even this last remaining feature would not presently be claimed as a distinguishing character. Indeed the skeleton of *Archaeopteryx* is currently regarded as scarcely distinguishable from the dinosaur *Compsognathus.* As shown in Figure 4, *Archaeopteryx* is *Compsognathus,* but with feathers, the absurdity of whose supposed attachments lies clearly beyond the border of the ridiculous.

Figure 4: Archaeopteryx compared with *Compsognathus. Compsognathus* in black outline, *Archaeopteryx* in blue. (From J. J. Hublin, *Prehistoric Animals,* Hamlyn Encyc., London 1984).

Hesperornis had neither the feathers nor the mechanical power for flight. It was clearly a wading reptile, possibly equipped with membrane-covered wings that were used for paddling. *Ichthyornis* is said to have the mechanical power for flight but is without feathers, although on the doubtful authority of *Archaeopteryx* it is believed to have had feathers and to have flown. But with the feathers *Archaeopteryx* clearly a forgery, such a presumption for *Ichthyornis* largely loses its support.

Feathers are not an unmitigated blessing to modern water birds. Aside from the warmth conferred by feathers, which does not of course demand aero-dynamically-shaped feathers, ducks could move quicker if they were equipped with membrane-covered wings used as paddles in the fashion of a human butterfly swimmer. Nor are feathers an advantage for gliding purposes. No human hang-glider would think of preferring a feathered contraption to membrane-covered wings. Flight feathers

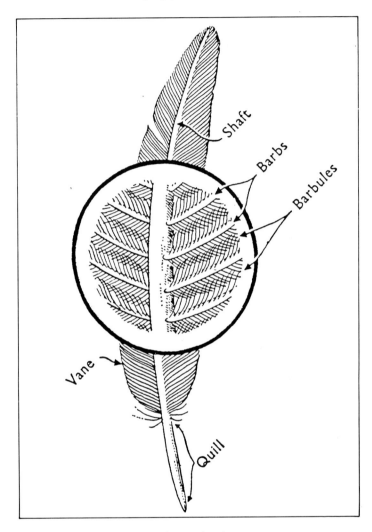

Figure 5: A Feather under the Microscope

The amazingly complex mesh of a vaned feather, as only a microscope can reveal it. The magnification shows how each barb of the vane is in effect a miniature feather. The top row of barbules, carried on the barbs, in turn carry minute hooks — the barbicels; and each hooked barbule interlocks with its unhooked neighbour on the next barb.

only make physical sense for a creature that is concerned with the subtler aerobatics of flight, so that to *begin* evolution towards flight with aerodynamically-shaped feathers is to put the cart a considerable distance in front of the horse. The beginning needs to come from paddling in water, at first weak paddling as with *Hesperornis*. So could the breast muscles required later for flight have evolved, with the final step to flight appearing either in the genetic storm at the Cretaceous-Tertiary boundary or in some later storm.

The flight feathers of a bird are constructed from a tough springy material with the structure and shape shown in Figure 5. We have found the number of barbs per unit length of the shaft to be remarkably constant from bird to bird — it was about 25 per centimeter both for an owl feather of length 4 inches and for a goose feather of length 12 inches. The under part of the shaft, the so-called ventral side, has a characteristic tapered depression that would produce two closely-spaced convergent narrow grooves in cases of feathers fossilised with the ventral surface facing into the rock, but with a single broader groove in cases where the upper or dorsal surface faced into the rock.

The delicate hollow bones of birds do not fossilise well. Nevertheless the bony skeletons of birds have been preserved in the fossil record in far greater number than have feathers. Few examples of fossilised flight feathers from before the Pleistocene have been found, except for *Archaeopteryx*, where, in total contrast to the rest of the fossil record, feathers are claimed in profusion, both perfect and modern, a situation that in most walks of life would alone be sufficient to arouse suspicion.

CHAPTER 2

Archaeopteryx –
A Preliminary History

The Jurassic system of sedimentary rocks was defined as early as 1829 and was the first to be given a geographic name, named after rocks that outcrop in the Jura mountains of Switzerland, with jura thought to be an old Gaulish word meaning 'forest'. The Jurassic period, extending from about 190 million years before present to 136 million years before present, has been intensively studied. It is divided into three major intervals, lower, middle and upper with the time-sequence going lower to upper in the opposite sense to that in which the rocks are revealed by erosion. Each of the major divisions of the Jurassic is then divided into a multitude of zones and sub-zones according to the nature of the fossil organisms found in the various strata.

Jurassic strata principally outcrop in Britain near Market Weighton in Yorkshire and in the Cotswolds, where Jurassic rocks provide the beautifully coloured stone with which Cotswold villages are built. There is also a major outcrop forming the Mendip hills and there are minor outcrops in Scotland and N. Ireland. Jurassic rocks in Europe partially encircle the Paris basin, while in Germany there are important outcrops in the south-west, none more so from the point of view of zoologists than the limestones of the Pappenheim district situated about

Plate I: A lithograph by Henri de Toulouse-Lautrec (1892), "The Englishman At The Moulin Rouge.".

40 miles south of Nürnberg. At Solnhofen on the River Altmüh, a tributary of the Danube, there are quarries of Jurassic limestone laid down about 160 million years ago, quarries containing fossils that are said to be the most perfect in the world.

Solnhofen limestone was also famous for its use in lithography, a form of reproduction in which print or an artist's drawing is marked with some ink-attracting greasy material on a smooth limestone surface. Water is then made to cover the non-greasy parts of the surface, with the water having the effect of repelling the ink and confining it to the marked regions. The method led to extremely faithful reproductions, with essentially no wear occurring to the limestone slab, and so permitting an almost unlimited number of copies to be struck from a single stone. Since colour could also be used, the lithographic process had great interest and potential for artists. Quality improved greatly during the second half of the 19th century, culminating in the now famous work of Henri Toulouse-Lautrec of which an example is shown in Plate I.

The owners of the Solnhofen quarries thus had outlets far more valuable for their stone than use as an ordinary building material, with the sale of fossils to museums an addendum to the sale of stone to the printing trade. Unlike the lithographic outlet which was open-ended with printers always needing more limestone slabs, the sale of fossils was unfortunately a saturating market. For one thing, fossils do not deteriorate — once in a museum or private collection they stay the way they are more or less indefinitely. For another thing, the exposed limestone strata at Solnhofen covers but a limited geological range and so could contain only the fossils of creatures living within that special range of time in that particular place. Hence both the market and the range of the supply were limited. Once museums and wealthy collectors had acquired all there was to acquire, the fossil outlet became essentially clogged, except in so far as new museums became established from time to time, but this would be slow business indeed. So what to do? Give up? Humans never give up, if there is a niche of profitable survival to be found they will find it. The trick was to invent fossils, basing them on genuine fossils acquired from the quarries. Besides which, it had for long been found that higher prices could be obtained for something weird and wonderful than for something ordinary and straightforward, provided museum directors could be persuaded into accepting the weird and wonderful. To aid acceptance, skills in forgery had been developed even as early as the 18th century, and indeed the whole area had become notorious for its cooperatives of skilled forgers long before the appearance of *Archaeopteryx* in 1861 (see for example H. Wendt, *Before the Deluge*, Victor Gollanz, London 1968, p. 54 *et seq.*)

An unintended side-effect of the publication in 1859 of Darwin's *The Origin of Species* was that it provided a charter for fossil forgers. By predicting the existence of transitional forms, links between known forms, it provided a clear target for the forgers, and with the important bonus that by fabricating transitional forms of the kind the scientific world was expecting to discover the forgers suddenly found themselves on the side of the angels, with support coming to them even from the world's most prestigious museums. It appears to be no accident that *Archaeopteryx* should have appeared so soon after *The Origin of Species.* In his well-known book *Life on Earth* David Attenborough writes: " . . . in a quarry . . . searchers discovered an almost complete skeleton of a feathered creature the size of a pigeon. It lay sprawling on the rock, . . ., and all around it the clear impress of its feathers . . ." So within less that two years of *The Origin of Species* what has been described as the most convincing example of Darwin's major prediction had appeared all open and sprawling on the rock, ready and waiting for the searchers to find it.

A single feather about two and a half inches long had already appeared in late 1860 or early 1861, very hard indeed on the heels of *The Origin of Species*. It was a completely modern feather, as of course it had to be because the forgers necessarily were obliged to work with modern feathers. It too appeared in poorly documented circumstances, and the manner in which it was sold and subsequently displayed broke what should properly be the basic rule of paleontology. When a piece of rock is split to reveal a fossil there should be two surfaces available for study, a so-called slab — usually the portion of the rock that was lower in the ground — and the opposite counter-slab. So long as the rock has been split cleanly, and we are told the quarrymen of Solnhofen were past masters at splitting slabs of rock cleanly, there must be a close matching of material texture in corresponding neighbourhoods all over the newly exposed surfaces, and the contours in corresponding neighbourhoods must be complementary to each other. These rigorous con-straints, so long as they were properly adhered to, set a severe problem for forgers, since a forger after making alterations to one portion of the fossil would be required to match his alterations exactly on the other portion, unless in some way he could contrive to prevent a comparison between the two portions from being made by a purchaser, or unless the purchaser didn't much care about making the comparison.

Three fossils bearing perfectly formed feathers appeared under poorly documented circumstances at the Solnhofen quarries between 1860 and 1877, and none with clearly marked feathers has appeared since. There was the single feather of 1860-61, the *Archaeopteryx* specimen of 1861, and a second even more expertly-executed *Archaeopteryx* specimen in 1877. The same family appears to have handled the disposal of all three specimens, obtaining very high prices by the standards of the day. Karl Häberlein was the medical officer for the Pappenheim district, and he seems to have obtained a corner on Solnhofen fossils generally, possibly through providing medical services for the quarrymen or conceivably as the spokesman for a cooperative. The slab of the single feather of 1860-61 went to the Münich Museum and the counterslab was sold to the Berlin Museum, thereby separating the two by what was a considerable distance in those days, and so effectively removing the possibility of a close comparison being made. We have not come on an explanation of how this trick was effected, or why the Directors of the two museums in question consented to it, thereby breaking what should be the first rule of paleontology, that slab and counterslab be kept together and displayed together. Had the two indeed been displayed together, the forgery would have been apparent, since the background rock texture is quite discrepant between the two parts, as can easily be seen from Plate II. Rock cannot split leaving a rough texture on one portion, as we see on the left side of Plate II, but with a smooth texture at corresponding places on the other portion shown at the right side of Plate II.

We suspect this forgery to have been perpetrated by someone who drew on a good knowledge of lithographic technique. The scenario went something as follows. A fine cement paste was prepared from ground-up Solnhofen limestone and the paste was smeared lightly on one portion of the split piece of rock. A feather was either carbonised itself or impregnated with a black sticky

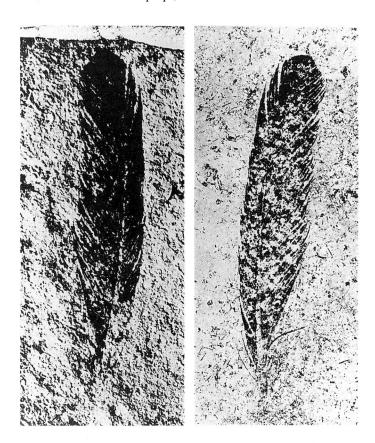

Plate II: The single feather which appeared in 1860-61, the slab on the left, counterslab on the right. Note the marked difference in the background texture of the rock, another commonsense indication of forgery.

carbonaceous material. The feather was then positioned ventral side down on the paste, and the other portion of the split rock was placed on top of the feather, with a light but firm pressure applied between the two pieces of stone. After the cement had set the two portions of the rock were separated again with the skill the local quarrymen are said to have possessed. The feather was now removed, leaving an imprint on the thin layer of set paste, and leaving matching carbonaceous material on both of the separated surfaces, but also leaving a tell-tale difference of texture on the surfaces, just as one sees in Plate II. Without spending any great measure of time and effort, Shirwan Al-Mufti has obtained the better-matching feather impressions shown in Plate III, thereby demonstrating that such a forgery would not have been unduly difficult.

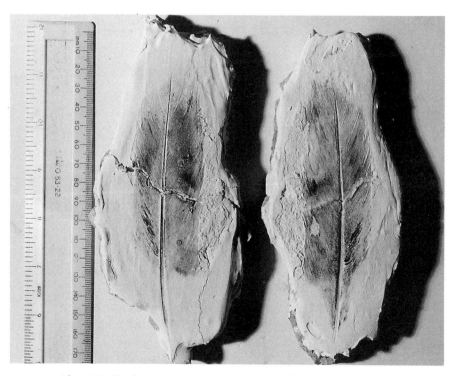

Plate III: Feather impressions obtained in a fine-ground paste by Shirwan Al-Mufti.

The *Archaeopteryx* specimen that appeared so remarkably in 1861, lying "sprawling on the rock" as David Attenborough puts it, was sold by Karl Häberlein in 1862 to the British Museum, for what at the time was considered to be a very large sum — it absorbed the Museum's free money for almost a two-year period. The museum did not make the mistake of acquiring only half a fossil, both slab and counterslabs were obtained. Since the two do not match today, and since they matched even less in 1862, the discrepancy would have been discovered by anyone who was permitted to examine the two parts carefully. Why the British Museum thus chose to acquire a discrepant fossil will form a part of our story. The fossil was acquired by Richard Owen, then the Superintendent of the Museum's Natural History section, about whom Thomas Henry Huxley had written: "He has been very civil to me, and I am as grateful as it is possible to be towards a man with whom I feel it necessary to be always on my guard." This was in 1851, nine years before Huxley's confrontation with Owen and Bishop Wilberforce at the famous Oxford meeting in 1860 of the British Association for the Advancement of Science.

On 20 November 1862, Owen read a paper to the Royal Society which appeared the following year in *The Transactions of the Royal Society* and was entitled: "On the *Archaeopteryx* of von Meyer, with a description of the Fossil Remains of a long-tailed species, from the Lithographic Stone of Solenhofen." The paper consists of fourteen pages of detailed description of the main slab of the fossil, but apart from a brief one-line mention in the notes to the Plates at the end of the paper nothing is said of the nature of the counterslab. The Plates contain an excellent draftsman's drawing of the main slab but not a drawing of the counterslab, an omission for which there is no explanation it seems except that something was seriously amiss already at the time the museum acquired the specimen. When we first read the literature on this whole subject we tried to half-excuse the omission by wondering if Karl Häberlein had tricked Owen into accepting the main slab only, just as in the case of the single feather sold to the Münich Museum. Perhaps Owen was embarrassed about the matter and was seeking to cover-up the absence of the counterslab we thought at first. But a search through the magazines of the period revealed a note in the *Edinburgh Review*, written in 1863 by an observer who attended the Royal Society meeting of November 20, 1862, according to whom both main slab and counterslab were indeed in the Museum's possession. So the explanation of the omission of effectively all mention in Owen's paper of the counterslab had to be more complex it seemed.

The incredibly perfect *Archaeopteryx* specimen of 1877 was sold for what was at that time an immensely large sum, 36,000 gold marks, sold remarkably enough by Karl Häberlein's son, Ernst, who appears to have followed his father in obtaining the fossil trade of Solnhofen. The slab-counterslab matching problem was eased for the 1877 specimen because the counterslab of that specimen is in pieces, and piecewise matching would be a less difficult problem for forgers than a sustained matching over the whole area of the fossil. The feather barbs on one of the wings of this Berlin specimen are exquisitely imprinted, with a resolution maintained over a considerable area of the stone surface as fine as one-fifth of a millimetre. How it was possible to split a chunk of rock to within an accuracy of a fifth of a millimetre on the one side, but yet to break-up the other side into gross lumps, would be seen by even a cautious person to require explanation.

For several years before the autumn of 1984 we had

regarded *Archaeopteryx* as a discrepant oddity but we had not thought of it as a fraud. One of us had written: "*Archaeopteryx*, the much-acclaimed link between reptiles and birds, is isolated in the fossil record. There are no steps in the record from reptiles to *Archaeopteryx*, or from *Archaeopteryx* to birds . . ." We by-passed the problem of *Archaeopteryx*, dismissing it in our minds as an irrelevant oddity until September 1984 when we received a letter from Lee M. Spetner in Rehovot, Israel. Dr Spetner wrote:

"For several years I have had a strong suspicion that the *Archaeopteryx* fossil is not genuine. . . I suspect that (the 1861 and 1877) fossils were fabricated by starting with a genuine fossil of a flying reptile and altering it to make it appear as if it originally had feathers."

Dr Spetner then offered to send us details of his arguments — if we should be interested. Replying that we were indeed interested, we subsequently received a manuscript in October 1984 which convinced us that a *prima facie* case existed for thinking *Archaeopheryx* a fraud. Dr Spetner also told us that he had been granted permission by Dr Charig at the British Museum to photograph the 1861 specimen, and we were eventually asked if we would assist in this project. We agreed and in the afternoon of 18 December 1984, Mr R. S. Watkins photographed the fossil over a two-hour period. When we gathered around the following day on 19 December to examine the resulting prints and slides it was immediately clear that Spetner's *prime facie* case (as set out in 1980 by Dr Spetner) had been considerably advanced, and that details were now revealed of a kind which had not hitherto been published, published for example in the pictures given at the end of de Beer's book of 1954. There is nothing in de Beer's photographs to tell one that mysterious, nearly straight edges are to be found in many places on the fossil, edges which are really very small changes of level, not cracks, and which seem to be the boundaries of thin layers of some agent, possibly varnish or latex rubber, which has been used to stick-down peeling areas of cement. De Beer's photographs are indeed defective in much less subtle matters than this. For instance, the picture given of the counterslab was obtained in a light that suppressed a considerable ridge structure in one of the wing areas of the counterslab, and since it happens that this structure was seriously discrepant from the main slab the omission was important.

Our first thought, hope if you like, held especially by Dr Spetner who had come over from Israel on the 18th and 19th, was that the Museum, on being presented with the facts and arguments, would agree to a collaborative project to test for the authenticity of the fossil, as for instance by comparing the fine-scale structure (if necessary at an atomic level) of the cement-like feather-bearing material with the structure of the surrounding rock. To this end, N.C.W made a journey to London in February 1985 to show senior museum staff the results of the photography. Their presentation led only, however, to the multiplicity of hypotheses which Ockham's razor is supposed to dispose of, so that this proferred olive branch withered before it had time to grow.

At the suggestion of Mr Watkins it was then decided to publish a selection of the new details in the *British Journal of Photography*, and five pictures accompanied by a bland text was eventually submitted to that Journal. The Editor, Mr Geoffrey Crawley, who has a considerable reputation for spotting frauds, instantly suspected fraud as soon as he saw our modest article, and thereon wrote a general press release saying as much. The media responded by taking the matter up and by making a nine

hour wonder out of it, something the media are particularly good at. If it did nothing else, the uproar served
to bring us to attention. To this point we had been
curious in a rather distant way. Now we resolved to make
a proper job of it, digging into the literature as well as
wringing every bit of evidence from the photographs in
our possession. The immediate outcome were three
further short articles sent to the *British Journal of
Photography*, articles that presented the case for fraud in
increasingly frank terms.

One of us (F.H.) happened to be in Washington D.C.
in early May 1985. A friend wished to visit the National
Museum of Natural History. Enquiry from a senior
official there revealed that the museum had a cast of the
main slab of *Archaeopteryx*, and an excellent cast it
proved to be, but the museum did not have a cast of the
counterslab the official said. So here was one of the outstanding museums of the world without reproductions of
both slab and counterslab of what is often said to be the
most famous of all fossils, a situation that by now we
thought curious.

The lighting of the cast of the main slab at the National
Museum of National History happened to be such that
the eye picked-out an interesting spot in one of the wing
areas. F.H. was much taken by what he had seen, or
thought he had seen, excited enough to make an
immediate transatlantic call to N.C.W., suggesting that
the British Museum specimen be re-photographed over
the area in question. Permission to re-photograph was
granted for the period 2.30 p.m. to 5 p.m. on 23 May
1985. Arriving at the museum at the appointed time we
were surprised to be asked to sit down to a roundtable
discussion with members of the Museum staff.

The atmosphere was not particularly cordial, and it
took up the first hour of the time we thought we had been

granted in which to photograph the fossil. But during this hour we were certainly told two things. First, that the Museum felt enough was enough, and this would be the last occasion on which access would be permitted to their fossil. The second thing we learned was that a layer of latex rubber had been applied to certain areas of the fossil, in connection with a program for obtaining special casts of those areas. When eventually we reached the fossil with about an hour to spare for photography we found that whatever had been seen in Washington D.C. could not now be seen because of a whitish pall covering the area in question. Other parts of the fossil had fortunately not been touched, however, and by this stage we had accumulated quite a number of sensitive points which could be subjected to explicitly-directed examination in the other untouched areas. As it eventually turned out, it was evidence from these other areas which gave proofs of forgery that should be sufficient to convince anybody who is not in the unfortunate condition of being professionally unconvincible. This further evidence will be described in detail in forthcoming chapters.

CHAPTER 3

Archaeopteryx –
A Preliminary Assessment

The Cambridge astronomer, Sir Arthur Eddington, used to interrupt the lectures he gave on general relativity during the nineteen-twenties and thirties with a story from the eclipse expedition at Principe in 1919. The purpose of the expedition was to test Einstein's prediction that light passing close to the sun would be bent in its track. Eddington's main companion at Principe was a practical chap, a Mr E. T. Cottingham from the Royal Greenwich Observatory. Eddington told of how, as he explained the epoch-making significance of the observations, Cottingham became more and more excited, eventually to the point where he forgot to remove the cover from the objective of the telescope at the critical moment of beginning of the eclipse. Eddington would then stand with a smile in front of the class and remark dryly that it was he, the theoretician not the practical chap, who had remembered to remove the cover, just in the nick of time. Modern astronomers with a bent for both theory and observation mostly take the moral of this story to heart, even if they never heard the story from Eddington, even if they never heard the story at all, for it is modern general practice to give full attention to the job in hand and not to be sidetracked into theorising in the middle of a practical job. Although we ourselves were fully aware of the wisdom of this practice, it was hard in the photographic sessions described in the preceding chapter not to be arrested by immediate impressions on our first view of *Archaeopteryx*. The first impressions were concerned with the tail area. The initial summation of what the eye saw and the brain calculated was that the thing was outrageous and could not possibly be true, especially when the main slab was taken together with the counterslab, as they are shown here in Plates IV and V.

Unless one is concerned with precise distances, it is useful to think of the tail as being about a foot long, taken from its root to the broad paddle-shaped end. The general scale of other components of the fossil are then intuitively apparent. The original piece of rock containing the genuine *Compsognathus* fossil was probably split with a bias of the bones towards the main slab, but the bias could not have been anything like so marked as we see in Plate IV, with many of the bones now lying in artificially dug channels. The cavities belonging to the tail vertebrae in the counterslab are deep enough to show that the original quarryman's splitting was not too far from being central to the fossil. The generally embedded look of the main slab is due, not only to the obviously dug channels, but to the forger(s) having excavated the wings and the tail areas. There can be no question about the excavation because the tail area is decisively lowered with respect to the surrounding rock, and the counterslab shows no corresponding raised area. We can dismiss from the outset therefore any suggestion that the fossil as we see it now was revealed all in a moment by a blow delivered by a quarryman to an original slab of rock. Particularly, the fine details of the feathered areas in the wings and the tail were not revealed by the quarryman, those in the tail lying

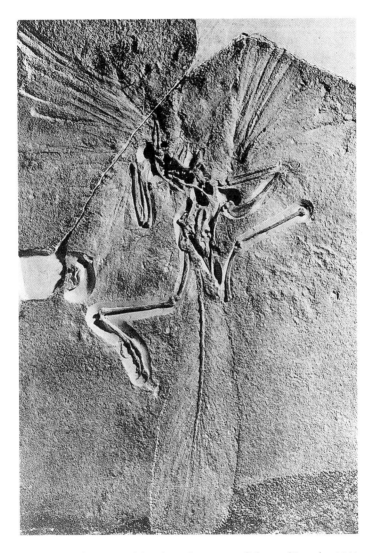

Plate IV: The main slab of *Archaeopteryx lithographica*, the 1861 specimen.

Plate V: The counterslab of *Archaeopteryx lithographica*, the 1861 specimen (Plates IV and V were obtained in circumstances to be described later in the text from photographs published by G. de Beer in *Archaeopteryx lithographica*, 1954, British Museum, Natural History Publication).

in the paddle-shaped depressed area not matched on the counterslab.

As we have remarked already, the feather impressions are exquisitely delicate — they are far too fine to be seen at the resolution of Plate IV. Details can be seen, however, in Plate VI. The left-hand part of Plate VI is about a third way up the tail as seen globally in Plate IV, to its left and in the same orientation. The right hand part of Plate VI is turned at right angles to the orientation of Plate IV and is the region of the latter to the right towards the end of the tail.

The first question which has to be answered by anyone with a belief in the authenticity of the fossil is how, with the face of the main slab having originally had much the appearance and texture of the counterslab in Plate V, was it possible to prise out from the sheer face of the rock (working 'normally' to the face as a geometer would say) further stony material with such extreme precision as to arrive at the unbroken fine details of Plate VI? Unlike metals which are comparatively strong whatever the forces acting on them, stone can be either strong or weak according to the nature of the forces. Stone is strong only with respect to compression, and architects seeking to erect large buildings in stone alone must ensure that over all parts of the building the stone is held against gravity by compressive forces. In ancient times this made for quite a problem in building a stable arch of stone above a door-way, and in medieval times it made an immense problem in building the high roofs of cathedrals. Wooden rafters helped of course, thus breaking out of the use of stone alone, but creating the fire hazard which recently gutted York Minster. Stone is so weak in tension, on the other hand, that forearms drops easily off stone statues, unless once again the sculptor contrives a design that provides a compressive force in support of the arms. Even such small pieces of stone as the noses of statues drop off easily. Stone is also weak with respect to shear forces. Imagine a plane running through a piece of stone and then put forces on the stone parallel to the plane, arranging in some way for the direction of the force to jump from being in one direction to being in the opposite direction as you go across the plane. By this means you have a shear across the plane. Sedimentary rocks are particularly weak with respect to shear when the chosen plane is a so-called bedding plane. At any pause in the deposition of the soft material which subsequently hardened to form the sedimentary rock there was an upper surface that was approximately a plane. Such approximate planes, corresponding to fluctuations in the deposition rate of the sediments, are the bedding planes of the resulting rock. By striking a lump of sedimentary rock with closely-spaced bedding planes hard at its outer boundary, it is easy to split it along such a plane, and a skilful stone mason can split the rock fairly close to any particular plane you care to specify. This explains why the Solnhofen quarryman who split the genuine *Compsognathus* fossil managed to hit the central level of the tail vertebrae so closely.

What you cannot do, what nobody can do, is to attack the open face of a piece of stone in any easy way. A stone mason may wish to produce a design in a face of stone, and on a more delicate level a sculptor may also want to produce an image on a surface, but in such cases the mason or sculptor has to go at the stone in a most determined fashion with a hammer and chisel. This is because they are attacking the material under compression. They are attacking the stone where it is strong, and every sculptor will tell you that the hammering and chiselling is back-breaking work.

That considerable force was indeed required to attack

Plate VI: Two enlargements of the tail area of *Archaeopteryx*, the first panel being to the left and the second panel to the right of the tail itself, with the latter turned at right angles to the standard orientation of Plate IV.

the stone face of *Archaeopteryx* is proved by the vigour of the chisel marks to be seen around the feathered areas, whether in the wings or the tail, material being dug-out to a depth of about three millimetres in those areas. The left panel of Plate XVI, showing the chisel marks at the extremity of the upper left wing, establishes this situation beyond any doubt.

If the fossil were genuine, we would have to suppose that, with the boundaries of the feathered areas brusquely dug-out, thin layers of rock were then levered away with the precision required to reveal scores of feathers and tens of thousands of feather barbs. The barbs and the spaces between them form remarkably even sequences of ridges and valleys. This uniformity, maintained everywhere to within a small fraction of a millimetre, would be consistent with the result of artificially pressing feathers into a soft surface which subsequently hardened, as shown by the simulated impressions of Plate III, but would be beyond reasonable probability for the excavation of an actual fossil. An attempt to 'prepare' upwards of 10,000 feather barbs would lead to a more broken situation, with barbs revealed in places where the 'preparer' was lucky, but with gaps and tears in other places.

It is unquestionable that the fossil as we see it today did not appear all in a moment with the blows of the quarryman's hammer. If the fossil is genuine, it was prepared with extreme skill in a task that must have occupied the preparer for a very considerable period of time. Only if the preparer, after carefully revealing the immense number of feather barbs with watchmaker precision, had then returned the fossil to the Solnhofen quarry and had casually left it there for a visiting party to discover could the fossil have been found in the circumstances described by David Attenborough, "sprawling on the rock. . . and all around it, dramatically and indisputably, the clear impress of its feathers." If Mr Attenborough's story is correct, as we think it is, then what was discovered was a forgery, since no preparer in his senses would return a genuine fossil, on which much delicate work had been done, to the vagaries of exposure to wind and weather, and perhaps to further blows of the quarryman's hammer.

There is another aspect of the tail of *Archaeopteryx* which the brain judges to be peculiar to the point of impossibility. The whole thing, all the apparent feather barbs, are everywhere in a single nearly flat surface, and moreover they are arranged in a highly ordered manner. Actual feathers do not have their barbs in a nearly flat surface. Feathers are quite springy objects, springy enough to prevent them from being pressed flat by immediately surrounding mud. Feathers might in principle be pressed flat by a large overburden, but any large overburden acquired quickly, as for instance by the body of a creature being covered suddenly in a mud chute, would be expected to lead to higgledy-piggledy orientations of the feathers, while an undisturbed rain of fine particles would encase feathers too gently to produce a uniform flatness over a fossil everywhere. Because of the fineness of Solnhofen limestone it is the latter situation that one should probably visualise in the present discussion. Every feather would therefore cut in a complicated way through a sequence of planes, which is just what practical fossil hunters say they normally find with respect to details of structure. When a rock is split open only a fraction of the details are recorded at the particular surface of cleavage. The bulk of the details still lie embedded in the rock matrix below and above the surface of cleavage. It would be impossible we think for a bird-like creature to fossilise in such a way that the impressions of tens of thousands of feather barbs were all confined in an ordered way to a single surface, even if it be

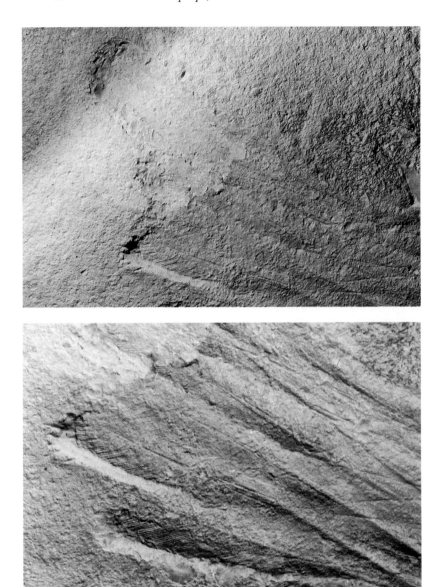

Plate VII: Enlargements of the upper left wing area of the main slab.

Plate VIII: The upper panel shows the upper left wing of the counter-slab. The piece of paste, shown in enlargement in Plate IX, can be seen here, lying above and a little to the left of the centre of the photograph. The lower panel is at the middle of the right wing area of the counter-slab. There are light feather impressions, difficult to see.

supposed possible to find that initially unknown unique surface working inwards from the boundary of a chunk of rock. A forger, on the other hand, would have no option but to produce an essentially flat surface for all the feather impressions. The forger would begin for the tail area of *Archaeopteryx* by gauging out the rock, just as one can see in Plate IV from chisel marks all around the area (as we shall notice in the next chapter a fraction of these chisellings were done subsequent to 1862, but enough of them are original to the way things were in 1862 for the present statement to be correct). Considerable care was taken in the British Museum specimen not to disturb the unbroken vertebrae of *Compsognathus*, as layers of limestone were levered out to make way for the paste that was to be applied, paste of a similar kind to the stuff used in forging the single feather of 1860 (Plates II and III). Similar care was either not taken or was not necessary in the case of the forgery of 1877, which has a tail that is broken in several places. Modern feathers, possibly with some edges cut to make them look a little unusual, were then placed ventral surfaces down on the paste, and the counterslab — also smeared with paste — was placed on top of the main slab. Probably the weight of the counterslab was itself sufficient to flatten the feathers and to press them sufficiently firmly into the paste, but if not a suitable weight could easily have been added on top of the counterslab. As with the single feather of 1860-61, the paste was allowed to set, the weakly-joined pieces were again split open, and the actual feathers removed.

The process was not an unqualified success. Because the paste had effectively been keyed into excavated depressions in the main slab it stuck there. In suitable lights it is easy to find places where the paste was keyed into excavated depressions, as for instance the case shown in the upper panel of Plate VII, which is an enlargement of the left wing area of Plate IV, and with the obvious paste-like material shown in still greater enlargement in the lower panel of Plate VII.

All this was on the main slab. On the counterslab the paste was mainly not keyed into depressions, and unfortunately for the forgers it mostly fell off when the main slab was again split away. In a few places bits of paste remained, however, more as an embarrassment than an advantage. Perhaps the clearest example of a remaining bit of paste is to be found in the wing area at the upper left of Plate V. It is shown in the upper panel of Plate VIII and in considerable enlargement in Plate IX, where it appears like a piece of chewing gum smeared onto the rough rock. The feather-like pattern taken up by this bit of paste is clearly seen in the enlargement of Plate IX, where it shows in marked contrast to the surrounding genuine rock, which naturally carries no feather impressions since *Compsognathus* did not possess feathers. The only part of the counterslab where the forgers had any real success with their feather impressions was in the middle of the right-wing area of Plate V. The impressions there, shown in enlargement in the lower part of Plate VIII, are hard to see because the paste was thin, which was probably why it did not fall off in this region.

Karl Häberlein is said to have behaved in an odd manner over the 1861 specimen. While permitting visiting paleontologists to have a general view of the fossil, he would not permit them to study it in detail, or to make sketches of it. This would accord with his being aware of the several defects in the forgery of which the collapse of the paste off the counterslab must have weighed heavily on his mind. The defects put Häberlein on a razor's edge. Would he get away with it or would'nt he was the question? There is no doubt that Häberlein

Plate IX: Enlargement of the isolated smear of paste in the upper panel of Plate VIII, which the eye should see as *raised* above the background. Note that whereas the paste carries featherlike impressions there are none on the background rock.

would not have got away with it but for the unique moment immediately following the publication of *The Origin of Species* at which the forgery was perpetrated.

De Beer remarks of the single feather of 1860 (Plate II):
"Towards the base of the vane the barbs appear filamentous and project from the quill, unconnected with the vane. Near them on the slab are to be seen a number of filaments of a dark colour, probably derived from the same animal as the feather.

"The vane of the feather is dark brown in colour, the depth of the colour increasing towards the tip. The colour was ascribed by von Meyer to the pigment present in the feather during life."

The first paragraph here is an example of the ease with which a hypothesis is converted into a presumed reality. There is no evidence to connect "a number of filaments of a dark colour" with any animal. What there is evidence of, plain to be seen in Plate II, is that the texture of the background rock is grossly different between the two halves of supposed fossil. What happened was that bits of the carbonaceous material with which the forger had impregnated his modern feather got away during the forging process and then became pressed into the surrounding paste.

The second short paragraph quoted above raises several questions. Would a pigment in feathers really survive for 160 million years? Possibly, but if it did, how comes it that whereas the single feather of 1860 shows aggressive pigmentation almost to the point of blackness, there is no sign of a similar pigmentation in the many feathers of the *Archaeopteryx* specimens of 1861 and 1877? The feathered regions in the latter are whitish coloured with a gloss rather like a low-glaze porcelain, just as one gets on hardened paste made out of finely-ground Solnhofen limestone.

Compsognathus fell ventral side downwards, which is to say belly downwards, in both the *Archaeopteryx* specimens. The genuine parts of the specimens thus obliged the forgers to work with their modern feathers also ventral side downwards towards the main slab. Modern feathers have a groove on their under sides which if pressed into soft material produces a negative image with two narrow grooves that converge towards the tip of the feather. A close examination of the left-hand part of Plate VI shows such a convergence very well towards the tips of the feathers, but the situation goes wrong towards the shaft ends. Instead of two grooves diverging towards the shaft ends the central ridge between the flanking grooves has itself a groove down its own length. A similar 'double-struck' effect is to be seen all over the British Museum specimen, and we understand it is also present in the Berlin specimen but to a lesser extent. Plate X gives enlargements of the right wing area of the main slab of the 1861 specimen, with the double-strike phenomenon showing up clearly at bottom right of the higher magnification panel of the Plate.

De Beer describes the double-strike phenomenon as follows:

" . . . there is clear evidence that in some cases the impressions were 'double-struck' on the mud underlying the dying bird. An impression of a rachis without any barbs attached to it may be seen close and parallel to another impression of a rachis from which barbs project in the normal manner. The impressions of the barbs are seen to cut right across the first impression of the rachis, which could not possibly have occurred unless the impression of the rachis had been made first and then, by displacement of the feather, the impression of the barbs had been superimposed on that impression."

The requirement for the stems or rachis of the feather

(see Figure 5, Chapter 1) to have left a double impression is clear from Plate X. Having arrived at this correct first step it is strange that de Beer did not continue to the obvious next step, namely that a double impression would be impossible under conditions of continuing sedimentation. Other authors have suggested the imaginary *Archaeopteryx*, having collapsed on a muddy surface in extremis, gave a final flap of its wings — the death beat it has been called — causing the feathers to shift slightly in their muddy grave. But under continuing sedimentation the first set of impressions left by the stems of the feathers would fill with mud, so that in the end it would only be the final positions of the feathers that would appear in the fossil. Besides which, why would only the rachis and not the barbs of the first position be preserved?

Let us try to imagine how the forgers operated. Limestone paste spread on slab and counterslab, feathers were then placed ventral side downwards in the wing areas of the main slab and in the excavated paddle-shaped tail, placed let us note without there being any convincing attachments from them to the genuine *Compsognathus* fossil, with the tail feathers sprouting inconsequentially out of the tail vertebrae of the unfortunate creature instead of there being proper muscular tissue wherewith to operate the feathers. Self-respecting forgers presumably had their doubts about such an absurd arrangement, but knowing what the savants were expecting they went ahead, we can only suppose with a sad shake of the head.

The last step was to lower the counterslab on top of the main slab. This ultimate stage of the operation had to be controlled with precision, because as the gap between the two slabs closed the springy feathers with their curled three-dimensional shapes would come under pressure and

Plate X: Enlargements of the right wing area of the main slab of the British Museum specimen, with the 'double-struck' effect showing clearly at the bottom right of the second panel.

would shift seriously unless the increasing pressure on them were applied carefully. A botch of a job had to be avoided at just this stage, for if the operation were unsuccessful, if the feathers shifted unacceptably, if the paste then dried with plainly wrong impressions in it, the operation would have been hard to repeat. *Compsognathus* would not stand up to too many mistaken bites at the cherry. So the counterslab was lowered with extreme care, with the forgers looking anxiously into the closing gap to check that nothing was going seriously amiss with the feathers. There would be a last moment at which the situation could be monitored successfully, with the pressure partially on the feathers and with them straightening and beginning to bite into the soft paste. It would be almost inevitable that the forgers would stop the closure of the slabs for a brief while at this stage, to make one last check on the situation. So the downward motion of the counterslab would be briefly interrupted, and would then be resumed after the check had been made, with the slabs coming together at last. It would be this momentary pause for final checking, with the feathers already partially biting into the paste, that would cause a very slight shift of some of them, the ones we now see double-struck in the supposed fossil. And because the full pressure was not yet on the feathers at the moment they shifted, impressions of the barbs were not yet made at this stage, a critical point indeed. Only the rachis had made marks in the first of the two positions, the barbs only appearing in the second position when the pressure was fully on. The impressions of the barbs in the second position would then cross-over the positions where the rachis had been in the first position, just as de Beer says in the above quotation.

Experience shows that slightly complex arguments like this last one give those who care nothing for Ockham's razor the opportunity to invent a multitude of supposedly saving hypotheses. So as well as trying to understand the intricacies of the details, it is as well also to have several broad unavoidable arguments. One such argument was there already in the global views of slab and counterslab shown in Plates IV and V. The odd thing is that one could easily stare at these photos for a week and not notice it, for as every conjuror knows, it is the most barefaced tricks that are the hardest to spot. We ourselves failed to notice the obvious until it was pointed out to us by Lee Spetner.

The outlines of the slab and counterslab do not match below the tail. Given this almost trivial remark, it is easy, by comparing Plates IV and V to see that the main slab has more to it than the counterslab. Moreover if you draw a line on the main slab corresponding to the boundary of the counterslab (for the region of the latter immediately below the markings of the tail vertebrae) it is immediately apparent that the line almost exactly follows the boundary between two quite different rock textures. What are these different textures one then asks?

If the chunk of rock that was subsequently split to reveal the slab and counterslab of the 1861 specimen had lain around in the Solnhofen quarry for many years before being noticed, and if the bottom part of what is presently the counterslab had already been knocked away, it might be possible to argue for a difference of texture on the ground that the bottom part of what is presently the main slab had experienced weathering, so that an identity of texture between what was exposed and what was still hidden within the chunk of rock would not be expected. Neither of the accounts we have seen of the discovery of the 1861 specimen is consistent with this possibility, however. As we quoted in Chapter 2, David Attenborough says the fossil on the main slab already lay open "sprawling on the rock" when the searchers found it, while Wendt (*Before the Deluge*, page 228) says: "'From a depth of sixty-five feet the workmen in the Solnhofen quarry brought up a slab which showed a nearly complete skeleton, minus the head, of the ancient bird . . .'" Although entirely different one to the other these stories could well both be partially true, with Wendt's account belonging to the original discovery of the genuine *Compsognathus* and Attenborough's to a subsequent-staged discovery of the forged *Archaeopteryx*. If Attenborough's description of what happened with respect to *Archaeopteryx* is correct, as we think it very probably is, then Wendt's story is seriously misleading, since by transferring the circumstances of the true discovery to the fake it gives unwarranted verisimilitude to the fake.

No claim for weathering as an agent in explaining the gross change of texture in the lower tail area of the main slab can be given credence from what is said about events at the Solnhofen quarry. The issue must be judged from undeniable evidence such as we see in the upper panel of Plate XI. This is an enlargement of the lower right hand region of the tail as seen in the global picture of Plate IV, printed here upside down — that is to say with the tail upwards. This reversal of orientation makes it easier in our experience for the brain to judge the shadows correctly. (The feather impressions of the tail at right are in low ground, and the curious mozaic pattern at upper centre and left form high ground.) Plate XI shows that delicate feather impressions continue without change across the line defined by the boundary of the counter-slab. Hence there can have been no appreciable weathering (if the feather impressions are genuine). Besides which, excess weathering of the bottom of the main slab would have produced low ground relative to

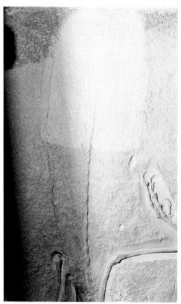

Plate XI: The upper panel is an enlargement of the tail area to the left in Plate IV, turned upside down here. The photograph shows the curious change of texture occurring near the bottom of the tail. The lower panel shows the 'white pall' encountered on 23 May, 1985, which curiously enough had the effect of bringing out a white line along the boundary where the texture changes so drastically.

less weathered parts of the main slab, whereas the curious mozaic pattern seen in Plate XI forms raised ground. Evidently then, the weathering story does not hold water, or anything else.

One has the impression in Plate IV of a distinct line of demarcation lying immediately above the dark mozaic material at bottom right of that Plate. The end of this line of demarcation as it reaches the tail area is also distinguishable in the upper panel of Plate XI, although not with the certainty needed for a positive conclusion. But the line of demarcation can be seen without cavil in the lower panel of Plate XI. It can also be seen emerging from the tail area at upper right.

When the genuine *Compsognathus* fossil, obtained quite possibly from sixty-five feet down in the Solnhofen quarry as Wendt says, came into the hands of the forgers it was found that the main slab was not large enough to accommodate the grandiose tail that was being planned. With more than a century of experience behind them, the forgers knew it was essential not to think trivially, so the grandiose tail it had to be. No matter that the main slab was too small. An extra piece of stone was simply cemented on. Inexperienced persons would have thought to cement on as carefully a matched piece of stone as possible. The forgers knew, however, that a match that was not a perfect match would be more likely to arouse suspicion than the most flagrant mismatch would do. Like the expert conjuror, they knew barefaced tricks deceive an audience best, and they proved right. Commentators have noticed fine details such as the double strike of the feathers discussed above, but nowhere that we have seen has there been even a passing mention of the huge change in texture at the bottom of Plate IV, or of the curious point noticed by Spetner, namely that the texture jumps at just the line which corresponds to the boundary at the bottom of the counterslab.

The reader will wonder why we have chosen to use so poor a photograph in the lower panel of Plate XI. This picture shows the white pall mentioned in Chapter 2 that we encountered on 23 May 1985, the pall which made it impossible to secure good pictures of the area of the fossil we had come particularly to examine on that occasion. It chanced, however, that the material put on the fossil by the Museum, the material producing the white pall, also had the effect of bringing out with satisfactory clarity the line of demarcation discussed above. Without the white pall we would hardly have been able to expose this aspect of the forgery so readily.

CHAPTER 4

Archaeopteryx –
A Changing Fossil over the Years

We have not been able to find photographs of the 1861 *Archaeopteryx* taken as it was received in 1862 by the British Museum. But as we remarked in Chapter 2 the paper published by Richard Owen in the *Transactions of the Royal Society* had a draftsman's drawing of the main slab of the fossil, the drawing shown here in Plate XII. A number of common features between Plate XII and the modern photograph of Plate IV can readily be distinguished, and distances between them measured accurately on both Plates. We found that ratios between such measured distances are the same to within fine margins for the two Plates, a result which confirmed our general opinion that no draftsman employed in 1862 to produce a drawing for the *Transactions of the Royal Society* would offer anything but near-perfect work. We concluded therefore that Plate XII shows how the main slab looked at the time the 1861 *Archaeopteryx* was acquired by the British Museum.

As well as similarities between Plates IV and XII there are differences. In Plate XII the bones lie neatly on the slab, whereas the centre of Plate IV is a chaos of bones, a midden produced by repeated excavations of the fossil over the past century and a quarter. Since the excavations have done nothing but bring to light the skeleton of the

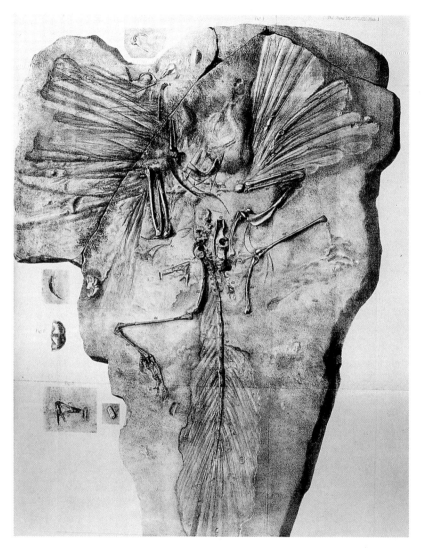

Plate XII: The 1862 drawing of the main slab of *Archaeopteryx lithographica.*

dinosaur *Compsognathus*, a specimen of which could have been acquired independently by the Museum, it would evidently have been better if *Archaeopteryx* had been left in the condition of Plate XII.

The upper left wing areas of Plates IV and XII are notably different. An enlargement of this area is shown in the upper panel of Plate XIII, together with an enlargement of the right wing area of the counterslab in the lower panel. If the counterslab were placed on the main slab these two wing areas should fit snugly together, and to within the accuracy one can judge by eye from the two panels of Plate XIII they would indeed do so. There is the trouble, however, that the upper left wing area of the main slab is not the same today as it was in 1862. Instead of giving a good match to the counterslab, the upper left wing area of the drawing of Plate XII has an outline when fitted over the corresponding upper right-wing area of the counterslab given by the light broken line of Plate XIV, the heavy broken line being the way things are today. That is to say, the upper left-wing area of the main slab has been changed since 1862, changed in such a way that its outline when fitted over the counterslab has been altered from the light broken line of Plate XIV to the heavy line.

The discrepancy was so startling that we felt compelled to wonder if the draftsman of 1862 might not have made a mistake after all. As luck would have it again, however, we chanced on an old plaster cast of the main slab of the British Museum specimen, long taken out of display in the Cardiff Museum and stored away in the basement there. The cast was identical to the draftsman's drawing. Draftsmen in the days of Bob Cratchett could not afford to make mistakes.

This discovery of the early plaster cast raised a new set of questions as well as emphasising that the main slab of the fossil (as it was received by the British Museum in 1862) did not fit the counterslab. While it could be argued that the major discrepancy shown in the upper panel of Plate XIV arose from a 'preparation' in which some three millimetre thickness of material was removed from an area bounded by the thin broken line of Plate XIV, such an argument necessarily implied yet again that the fossil could not have been discovered in the dramatic circumstances which have been reported, unless of course it was a forgery with which the Solnhofen quarry had been salted in advance of its supposed discovery.

The feather impressions to be seen today in the area of the main slab between the thin and thick broken lines of the upper panel of Plate XIV are dominated by the barbs of a single feather. The base of this feather can be seen on the early plaster cast, and what can indeed be seen there is both curious and suspicious. Although the cast, if taken at face value, implies vigorous tooling at the boundary of the thin broken line, the vigorous tooling has not cut into the feather impressions as they abut the boundary. The feather impressions must of necessity continue beyond the boundary of 1862, a situation that evidently invited the area between the present boundary and that of 1862 to be excavated. If innocent of mind, why would the 'preparer' not have continued to reveal the whole of this feather, especially in view of the great effort which must otherwise have been expended on the rest of the fossil? Rather does the lower unbroken portion of a feather, disappearing at the 1862 boundary, look like a rather obvious 'come-on'.

The lower panel of Plate XIV shows the left-wing area as we see it today, with the boundary of 1862 marked across it. We repeat that, if the fossil were genuine, the main slab was first cut-out to a depth of about three millimetres at this marked line, which process must have left a

Plate XIII: The first panel is the upper left-wing area of the main slab, and the second panel is the upper right-wing area of the counter-slab.

clear gash across the feather impressions. Yet the feather barbs continue unbroken across the 1862 boundary, another sufficient demonstration, one might think, of forgery. What the forger actually did was cut-out material, not in the 1862 boundary at all, but at the present-day boundary, or close to it. The feather impressions were then fabricated, along with the rest of the impressions over the whole face of the fossil. Then a 'come-on' was set-up in a few particular regions, notably at the upper right of the tail area and in this upper left-wing area. The feather impressions in these areas were first covered by a layer of organic material, which one can think of for convenience as equivalent to a thin layer of polythene — a protective layer where slip would be easy.

A granular rather than a fine-ground paste was then applied on top of the organic layer, so as to return the upper surface to the original form as close as possible, and as a finishing touch light pressure was applied from the counterslab, in order to create the appearance of an approximate match of slab and counterslab. After the paste had set, it was finally given a surface texture that matched the surrounding rock, a process in which fossil forgers are said to have been adept, even as early as the 18th century.

This first discovery on our part, that the fossil of 1861 had been changed, subsequent to its purchase by the Museum, came as a considerable surprise, though Lee Spetner had warned us that it might be so. Once several hands become involved, the trail of discovery is made much more complex, a point that was well taken in the classic form of detective story, where convention required that there should only be one murderer. Lee Spetner's suspicion that there might have been more than one murderer led him in December 1984 to ask the Museum if details of subsequent changes could be supplied.

At this point it is relevant that on both the 18th and 19th of December 1984 Spetner had asked at the Museum if details could be supplied to him of the changes the Museum had itself made to the fossil. A week or two later he also wrote a formal letter with the same request, receiving in reply only a copy of some pages from de Beer's book which makes but a passing reference to a 'preparation' of the fossil done by F. O. Barlow and L. E. Parsons and which of course we had in our files already. The book does not give the date of the 'preparation' but from extraneous evidence we think it must have been about 1925.

For a while we thought it had been the activities of Barlow and Parsons that had changed the 1861 *Archaeopteryx*, where the forgery was fairly easy to see, to a form in which the original discrepancy was hidden, or at any rate hidden unless one had the fossil in one own hands and could make really sensitive comparisons between the main slab and counterslab. The reluctance of the Museum to supply us with proper information in reply to Spetner's request turned out to be unfair to Barlow and Parsons, for eventually we discovered a contribution to a publication *Natural Science* containing the first photograph of *Archaeopteryx* we have yet found. The photograph appearing in an article by C. H. Hurst entitled *The Structure and Habits of Archaeopteryx*, is reproduced here in Plate XV. Both the upper left wing area and the outline of the tail are changed from the draftsman's drawing, and from the early plaster cast to the shapes we see today. Since Hurst's article appeared in 1895, the 'preparation' of 1925 had nothing to do with this first major change of the fossil.

Some feather impressions are to be seen in parts of these changed areas, in an area of the tail at its upper right and in the critical region at the top left. These impressions have barb spacings that are coarser in some places than anywhere else on the fossil. It is also in these places that curious layers of a sticking material are to be found. The upper panel of Plate XVI shows an enlargement of the top left wing protuberance, and the bottom panel shows the tail area in question. Both have the mysterious sticking material, edges of which can just be seen in the reproductions, looking in the upper panel of Plate XVI as if the sticking material had been used to stop thin strips of a white material that bears feather impressions from peeling away.

At this point it may be appropriate to comment generally on our photographs. In attempting to see the finest details on the rock surfaces have had the frustrating impression of feeling the camera was always

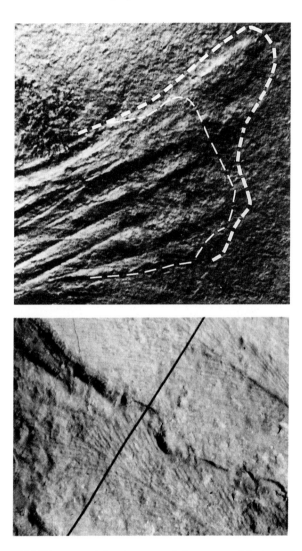

Plate XIV: The upper left-wing area of the counterslab shown in the top panel in reversal so as to compare outlines with the corresponding right-wing area of the main slab. The light broken line shows the situation in 1862, the heavy line as it is today. The bottom panel shows the left-wing of the main slab today, with feather barbs crossing the 1862 boundary and giving no sign of damage at that boundary. There should have been more appreciable damage if the impressions were genuine.

Plate XV: The first photograph we have found of the British Museum specimen of *Archaeopteryx lithographica.* Dating from 1895, the photograph shows that substantial changes were made between 1862 and 1895, particularly in the discrepant upper left-wing area.

slightly out of focus. This might have been true in a few cases, but it could not be true for every photograph. Besides which, bones always appear with clarity in the pictures, proving there was nothing wrong with the focus of the camera. Eventually we came to the conclusion that the rock is essentially covered everywhere with nearly translucent layers, whether of latex rubber, a varnish or sundry stone washes of some kind, with the several layers producing multiple reflections that have the combined effect of destroying any possibility of obtaining sharp focus.

Since it is now accepted that the skeletal features of *Archaeopteryx* are, with only one still debatable feature, the furcula or wishbone, indistinguishable from those of a known dinosaur, it is difficult to understand why over more than a century experts made such heavy weather of it. Richard Owen, who purchased the 1861 *Archaeopteryx* specimen on behalf of the Natural History Section of the British Museum and who subsequently became its Director, asserted that the bones of *Archaeopteryx* are hollow. Since the bones of *Archaeopteryx* are said in later publications not to be hollow, and since the matter should have been easily demonstrable from microscopic sections of the bones, something of a problem for the reader is posed already.

Coming forward almost a century to 1954, to the book of de Beer that we have mentioned a number of times, the situation is not a great deal better. The book is nine-tenths a description of *Compsognathus*, about which there is no debate. Under the guise that a remarkable creature of the utmost significance is being discussed, a lengthy anatomical description of a known dinosaur is given. Then in the one-tenth of the book when de Beer discusses the special features of *Archaeopteryx* little that has proved to be correct is said.

Aside from the feathers, de Beer lists three skeletal features of an avian character which distinguish *Archaeopteryx* from a reptile, in his opinion. The third of de Beer's characters, the hallux, a bone formation in the feet that would have permitted *Archaeopteryx* to perch on the bough of a tree in the manner of a bird, has died a quiet death. Neither J. H. Ostrom in a detailed technical discussion (*Collected Papers in Avian Paleontology, Smithsonian Contributions to Paleobiology*, No. 27, 1976), nor A. J. Charig in a more popular work *(A New Look at the Dinosaurs*, Wm. Heinemann 1979) make anything of it.

The first of de Beer's supposed avian characteristics, the pubis, has had an interesting subsequent history. The pubes are bones at the base of the spine that are directed backwards in birds but downwards and forwards in reptiles. The pubes in the 1877 Berlin specimen were reported to be directed backward in an avian orientation, so that possibly de Beer was relying on the Berlin specimen, although he gives the impression, but without saying so explicitly, that the British Museum specimen is the same in possessing pubes that are directed backwards like birds. This could not be decided, however, from the 1861 fossil as it was originally received in London, and if there were anything in de Beer's claim it had to be based on subsequent excavations, which in our opinion only produced an undocumented chaos of bones. It was also from the chaos of bones that de Beer claimed the 1861 specimen to have possessed a so-called sternum to which feathers could have been attached. In the publication cited above, Ostrom denies this claim, saying: "Contrary to de Beer's (1954) interpretation, no sternum is preserved in any of the presently known specimens of *Archaeopteryx*."

In the early 1970's, Ostrom examined the pubes of the

Plate XVI: An enlargement in the first panel of the upper tip of the left-wing area of the main slab, showing peeling areas and sticking material. This is a region excavated between 1862 and 1895. Note the vigour of the chiselling, showing beyond doubt that considerable force was required to attack the slab face-on. The second panel is the upper-right of the tail area, with a mysterious 'edge' running a slanting nearly-straight line down the central regions of the photograph from left to right. Note the differences of colour and texture on the two sides of this line, showing that it is not a hairline crack.

Berlin specimen, finding that although the bones were indeed directed backwards they were broken and had been rotated from a more downward orientation. We find it curious that Professor Ostrom apparently did not recognise his discovery as evidence of fraud, but when one is educated in beliefs shared by one's professional colleagues, when those beliefs are supported by long-established prestigious organisations like the Berlin and

British Museums, it is probably difficult to make a transition to a mode of thought that any scientist would find distasteful. Of his discovery, Professor Ostrom wrote (in *Annual Review of Earth and Planetary Sciences*, 1975, page 70):

"The one apparently avian aspect of the pelvis of *Archaeopteryx* is the backward orientation of the pubis preserved in the Berlin specimen. Elsewhere, I have tried to show that the pubis of the Berlin specimen is not preserved in its natural position. The correct orientation is not known (the pubis is displaced, or the complete pubis is not preserved in all presently known specimens), but all available evidence in the five *Archaeopteryx* specimens indicates that it probably was directed downwards nearly perpendicular to the sacral axis, or possibly even down and forward as in all theropod dinosaurs."

Mention of *five* Archaeopteryx specimens will surprise the reader. The difference between our two and Ostrom's five lies in the clarity of the feather impressions. The 1861 and 1877 specimens both have a multitude of impressions, including both rachis and barbs, the others have impressions visible only to the eye of faith. Thus Ostrom writes (same reference):

"If feather impressions had not been preserved in the London and Berlin specimens, they (the other three cases) would never have been identified as birds. Instead, they would unquestionably have been labelled as coelusosaurion dinosaurs. Notice the last three specimens to be recognised were all misidentified at first, and the Eichstätt specimen for 20 years was thought to be a small specimen of the dinosaur *Compsognathus*."

Judging by the pictures we have seen, one of the three specimens, discovered in 1956 and reported by F. Heller to have hollow bones and feathers (*Erlander Geol. Abhandlungen* 31, 1959) is in such poor condition that we would discount anything said about it — it is a first rule of science not to trust poor quality data. The so-called Eichstätt specimen found in 1951 is much better preserved. We have examined a good quality cast of it and can testify that the Eichstätt specimen has no feathers. There are short spicules emerging from the tail, which some have thought to be incipient feathers, but since similar spicules emerge from bones and from innocent cracks in the rock, both in this specimen and other Solnhofen fossils, no credence can be placed in such a claim — the spicules are probably mineral crystals, incipient dendrites, as seems obvious from colour photographs of the specimen. We have heard it said of the Eichstätt specimen that it originally bore feather impressions which were unfortunately destroyed in the 'preparation' of the fossil.

The fifth specimen was discovered long ago in 1855 and it resides in the Teyler Museum at Haarlem in the Netherlands. This Teyler specimen has been examined microscopically by Lee Spetner, and to the eye of a physicist it had no feathers, despite Ostrom's claim to have seen vestigial traces of the rachis of feathers (*Proc. Sect. Sci. Ned. Gkad. Wet B*, 1972, Volume 75).

Of the issues raised by de Beer in 1954 there remains the furcula or wishbone. The British Museum specimen possesses an overwhelmingly powerful furcula which the forgers of 1860-61 had no intention of being missed, as can be seen in the upper panel of Plate XVII. By 1877, the emphasis as to what was of interest to the savants had changed, however, to giving the forgers guidelines to produce a head with reptilian teeth, which was easy because *Compsognathus* really did have a reptilian head with teeth. So the 1861 specimen was given a robust furcula and no head in keeping with the spirit of the times, while the 1877 specimen had a head but no furcula

Plate XVII: The upper panel shows the massive furcula of the 1861 specimen of *Archaeopteryx*. Note the break in the bone at upper right, and the crack lower down the right-hand arm of the bone. The lower panel shows the cavity in the counterslab into which the furcula is supposed to fit.

obvious to the eye. We never cease to marvel at the ease with which inconsistencies like this appear to be accepted as a necessary concomitant of life in the biological sciences, a consequence we think of those sciences being based on a wrong theory. On the one hand, the 1861 and 1877 specimens are said to be fossils of the same creature. Yet on the other hand the specimen in London has a massive furcula — a supposedly important distinguishing feature of its avian status, not a side issue — while the specimen in Berlin has no such massive distinguishing feature.

In a paper communicated to the Royal Society in 1868, T. H. Huxley claimed the furcula of the British Museum specimen to be upside down from what it should properly be for a bird. De Beer suggested that perhaps currents in the water into which the creature fell contrived to turn the massive furcula, while leaving the more delicate bones of the rest of the skeleton unchanged in their orientations, a good example we feel of a vacuous hypothesis.

Actually it was somewhat unwise for the forgers to endow *Compsognathus* with a furcula, because a cavity had to be cut in the counterslab, with at least some semblance to providing a fit to the added bone. This would have to be done crudely with a chisel, which could not produce a degree of smoothness in cutting the rock similar to a true sedimentation cavity. Close examination of the furcula cavity cut by the forgers in the counterslab was one of our objectives when we were permitted to photograph the British Museum specimen on 23 May 1985, the result we obtained being shown in the lower panel of Plate XVII.

Before we discuss the details of Plate XVII there is simple evidence of forgery that should be mentioned. Turning back to the draftsman's drawing (Plate XII) it can be seen that the furcula at upper centre was originally free-standing on the main slab. It crosses over other bones and is not bedded firmly into the main slab. If the furcula were genuine, the real bed for it would be the cavity in the counterslab. But of course this was not a possible arrangement for the forgers, because the furcula did not fit properly into the counterslab, the cavity there being cut inevitably without the necessary precision.

If one imagines the counterslab placed on the main slab it would evidently be the left-hand side of the furcula that should fit into the right-hand side of the cavity, and *vice versa*. The cavity has a rock step in it at upper left, at a place corresponding to the break in the bone at its upper right. At lower right there is also a crack across the bone, with the region of the bone immediately above the crack looking as if it had been crushed. The draftsman's drawing of the furcula shows no crack or break, and since by this time we had developed an admiration for the accuracy of Bob Cratchett's friend we felt fairly certain that the furcula must have been broken at some time since 1862, and by some considerable force on so robust a bone, not simply by knocking out one's pipe on it. Our first thought was to take a look at the photographs at the end of de Beer's book. Plate VI there shows an enlargement of the region of the furcula, both for the slab and counterslab. Imagine our chagrin to discover that the pictures in de Beer were cropped so that precisely the parts of the furcula and cavity in which we were now so interested happened to be outside their printed boundaries by only a whisker.

It was at this point that we studied de Beer's photographs with something of the attention we had given to our own pictures. We were struck by a general monotonous greyness, and then by the inability of the eye to see any real detail. Although the picture of the main slab looked more or less allright at a first glance, it came as something of a shock to realise that we couldn't even tell the difference between shadows and dendritic crystals. How could this possibly be we puzzled? The photographic equipment available to the Museum should have been capable of needle-sharp focus. Moreover, the Museum photographers would have had ample time to set up special lights, which we could not do ourselves. So why were our pictures far richer in detail than de Beer's? We wondered for a brief moment if the trouble could have been a lack of reasonable quality paper for printing, but the thought had instantly to be dismissed. De Beer's book was excellently bound and the quality of the printed text was also excellent, as befitted what was clearly a prestige production by the Museum. At last, the almost incredible thought occurred to us: Had the pictures been downgraded by the addition of a monotone background? So convinced did we become that this postulate had to be true that we took de Beer's book to a standard photographic laboratory. Our instruction to the photographer there was simply to get the best reproductions from the pictures that he could. The result was an immediate and startling improvement of quality.

What was obtained by filtering out some form of monochrome background has been shown already in Plates IV and V, which still cannot be nearly as good as the pictures originally taken by the Museum's photographers. The reader will be most interested in the upper right wing area of the counterslab in Plate V, and in comparing this region with our own picture in Plate XIII. Whereas the right hand panel of Plate XIII shows a ridge structure curving upwards to the right, a structure it will be recalled that did not fit the main slab as it was received in 1862, nothing of this discrepant ridge structure can be seen in de Beer's photograph. One of the reasons why we needed access to the fossil on 23 May 1985 was to make certain, both by photography and by eye, that our picture of the ridge structure was correct. It was. Only by adjusting the lighting carefully were we able to suppress the discrepant ridges which show decisively that the fossil was forged.

Returning now to the problem of the breaks on the right-hand side of the British Museum's furcula, we soon found photographs which demonstrated yet again that the draftsman of 1862 had been correct. There are pictures of the furcula, unbroken, in the references cited above, in the book *A New Look at the Dinosaurs* by Charig and in Ostrom's contribution to *Collected Papers on Avian Paleontology*. Since it is reasonable to suppose that Charig in 1979 would not have used a very old photograph, the likely inference is that the furcula was damaged in recent years. We do not know how it was actually broken, cracked and crushed, but we can suggest a way in which it would be possible to produce the situation shown in Plate XVII. Simply take the furcula and press it with force into the cavity in the counterslab. The rough rock ledge in the upper half of the left side branch of the cavity would then produce just such a crack, a crushing, and a break as we now see.

We have remarked on the difference that whereas the Berlin specimen of 1877 possesses a head but no large furcula, the British Museum specimen possesses a massive furcula but no head, which raises the further question of whether the genuine dinosaur on which the British Museum specimen was based never had a head, an event to add to all the other oddities of the case. Or did the forgers simply lop off the head? There is evidence to indicate that the forgers were indeed so unfeeling as to have decapitated the fossil, because in the counterslab a little to the right of the middle there are scattered bones of the jaw of the creature together with five teeth, first noticed by Sir

John Evans in 1863 and reported by him in 1865 ("On the Portions of a Cranium and of a Jaw, in the (Counter)slab Containing the Fossil Remains of *Archaeopteryx*", *Natural History Review*, Volume 5, page 415, London and Edinburgh 1865). This makes it curious that evidence of the head should be absent on the main slab, except for a concretion at middle-left in Plate IV, a nodule known as the 'brain case', surrounded in Plate IV by an artificially-dug semicircular channel.

At the beginning in 1862 the 'brain-case' was said to be that of a bird, and most 19th century authors also appear to have thought the brain case distinctly bird-like, with affinities to the magpie being mentioned. As time went on, and in the opinion of paleontologists the skeleton became ever less bird-like, the thought of the brain case being like a magpie must have seemed unattractive. By the time of de Beer in 1954 the brain case had changed, in the ever-changing manner that is so characteristic of *Archaeopteryx*, to being dominantly reptilian, and by the time we come to Ostrom and Charig in the 1970's nothing is made of it at all.

Evolution from magpie brain to nothing-at-all is understandable if the 'brain case' were yet another forgery. The forgers affixed a bird-like cast in the separated place on the main slab where we see it in Plate IV. Because the brain of a bird clashed with the reptilian head of *Compsognathus* the head was removed, which is why the British specimen is headless. The birdlike brain case was a strong plus mark in the beginning, but as time went on into the 20th century the situation gradually changed, first to becoming neutral and at last to becoming a strong minus mark. So what to do? Simply remove the brain case, as was done a year or two ago. The upper panel of Plate XVIII shows the present state of affairs in the long-running saga of adjustments to

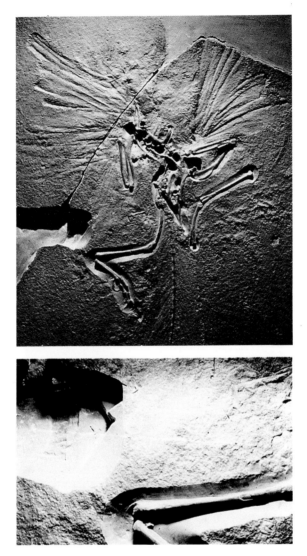

Plate XVIII: The upper panel shows the main slab of the British Museum specimen of *Archaeopteryx* as of 18 December 1984. The lower panel shows chisel marks in the cavity at left-centre of the main slab.

Archaeopteryx, with a whole chunk of the main slab now hacked away, even to the extent that the boundary of the main slab comes dangerously close to the left knee of the creature. It was explained in an earlier chapter that stone is strong under a compressive force. When attacked directly from the front the assault has therefore to be done in a determined way with hammer and chisel. The lower panel of Plate XVIII shows the vigorous assault that was mounted on this unfortunate creature, with extensive chisel marks to be seen in the bay at left-centre.

In December 1984 we had thought it possible to collaborate with the Museum on the physical investigation of the porcelain-like feather material of the fossil. We had envisaged obtaining about half a gram of such material wherewith to carry out a number of tests we had in mind. Although the visit to the Museum in February 1985, described in Chapter 2, was not encouraging, the question of collaboration resurfaced briefly in March and April, thanks to Mr Geoffrey Crawley, the Editor of the *British Journal of Photography*. However, in early May a letter was received from the Museum which put an end to such thoughts. It contained the following passage:

". . . you appear to be under a misapprehension concerning any tests that might be carried out on our *Archaeopteryx*. . . the question of who should do the testing is now irrelevant, for we have decided that any tests involving damage to the specimen, no matter how slight, cannot be justified on the grounds of necessity."

How it was possible to write of not causing the *slightest* damage to the fossil in the wake of the gross defacement shown in Plate XVIII we leave to the reader's judgement.

CHAPTER 5

Archaeopteryx –
Proof of Forgery and an Historic Interpretation

It is an engaging quality of decent persons that, despite an immense volume of contrary evidence in the history books, they still believe that authority can do no wrong. So very naturally the underlying feeling among decent folk will be that, despite all the admittedly interesting points we have raised in previous chapters, somehow it will eventually turn out that we have been fencing with the wrong end of the stick. Perhaps therefore we should offer a last shot in the hope of convincing the unconvincable.

Plate XIX compares the upper left-wing area on the counterslab of the British Museum specimen with the corresponding right-wing area of the main slab. If laid over each other in a manner that can be judged from their outer boundaries, after allowing for a different scale the two areas should match. There is an egglike hump to be seen for example over on the right of the main slab area that would fit into an oval depression of the counterslab area. As well as a match of ridges and grooves there should also be a match of dendritic patterns. These are the tree-like growths of dark mineral crystals which form a feature along the boundaries of both slabs. A close examination of the dendritic patterns shows an excellent match even of very fine details, except at the outer regions of the wings themselves. On the counterslab one sees extensive normal-looking patterns. But on the main slab one sees only a number of rather isolated black dots, the tree-like patterns are not formed so as to correspond even remotely to the counterslab. The wing area on the main slab carries feather impressions, and the paste used by the forgers to take up the impressions has largely covered the underlying matching dendritic patterns. The paste was thin towards the outer boundary where the feather impressions are almost vestigial, and from place to place where there was a high spot in the rock surface the dendrites break through the paste, to show as a number of more or less isolated spots. The proof of this can be seen in the two panels of Plate XX, which show two pictures of the outer part of the relevant wing area of the main slab, the two pictures being taken under slightly different lighting conditions. There are plenty of examples of marks to be seen showing faintly under the surface paste. These marks, if they could be fully seen instead of being half-masked by the paste, would form the dendritic patterns required to match the counterslab.

No affair of the magnitude we suspect we have touched on in this book could be entirely explained as a bit of trickery by a forger, or by a cooperative of forgers, and then by the later *amour propre* of the authorities in not wanting to admit that they had been deceived. Every museum has probably made a costly error at some time in the distant past, but without the mistake living on to haunt subsequent generations. A bigger circuit had surely to be involved somewhere.

One possible bigger circuit is the Darwinian theory of evolution by natural selection. The ancient doctrine of *cui bono* points squarely towards the supporters of that theory, for it is they who appear to have profited most from a belief in the authenticity of *Archaeopteryx*. More-

Plate XIX: The first panel is the upper left-wing area of the counter-slab, and the second panel of the main slab. Note the dendritic patterns along the cracks and outer edges.

over, supporters of the Darwinian theory have proved down the years to be just as doctrinaire and intolerant as was the theological establishment they replaced, so it is not hard to convince oneself that such zealots would go to great lengths to prevent the fraudulent origin of *Archaeopteryx* from being exposed.

When we first approached the question of historic motivation the case seemed to be already made for us. David Attenborough remarks in *Life on Earth* in connection with the 1861 appearance of *Archaeopteryx*:

". . . Huxley, Darwin's champion, had predicted that just such a creature must have existed, and had prophetically described its details."

Wendt in *Beyond the Deluge* writes similarly:

"When Thomas Henry Huxley tried to trace the derivation of birds from reptiles, he drew a sketch of a hypothetical primordial bird. It was a feathered creature with reptilian teeth, claws on the ends of the wings, scales on its body, and a long, lizard-like tail. Huxley had no idea that almost immediately afterward precisely such a primitive bird would be found, an animal that corresponded in almost all its details to his drawing. The only clue that existed at the time he wrote was the imprint of a small bird's feather."

The last sentence would place the time of Huxley's prediction as 1860-61, after the discovery of the single feather of Plate II, but before the discovery of *Archaeopteryx* in 1861. Added to these confident statements from Wendt and Attenborough, a well-known American paelontologist made the same statement about the prediction by Huxley to one of us (F.H.) in a verbal conversation.

We had learned several years earlier in attempting to form a judgement on a priority issue between Charles Darwin and Alfred Russel Wallace that in an historic question it is essential to go back to original documents, even though the process may be long and tedious. In this case, however, with the target clearly in view there seemed to be no problem at all. Besides which, there would surely have been quite extensive discussions of the situation in the newspapers and magazines of the day. A few hours spent in a library with material going back to the mid-19th century should suffice to settle the matter we felt. It was a considerable initial surprise when it did not. Week after week of sporadic visits to libraries brought us no nearer to success. A letter to David Attenborough met with the response that he felt the reference existed but could not put his hand on it all in a moment, and a telephone call to the American paleontologist met with the same reply. It is a pity that Wendt's book has no documentation, because if all the stories he tells could be supported by adequate references the book would be a goldmine of information. We have found ourselves that publishers often do not like books to be carefully documented, as they say readers find references to be off-putting. If so, let readers note that unsubstantiated stories have little value. Ideally, everything published should either be documented, or accompanied by an observational or experimental demonstration, or by a mathematical proof. Anything else is to reduce society to a guru culture. In this book we have therefore tried as far as we can to substantiate our main statements either by documentation or by visual evidence from photographs.

Balked eventually to the point of irritation, we spent independently a whole week on a library search, F.H. at the University Library in Cambridge and N.C.W. in Cardiff, Bristol and London. Still nothing. And the Librarian at Imperial College, London where Huxley's original papers are kept and have been classified, told us that he knew of no such reference. We can say therefore that either the story is a myth or the reference has been carefully and determinedly suppressed. If suppression is the answer, then the suppression would have had to be done by Huxley himself and it would have had to be done from the time of the discovery of *Archaeopteryx* onwards, because there is absolutely no mention of any such prediction in Huxley's technical papers thereafter or in the nine volumes or so of his published essays. Nor in any of the papers on *Archaeopteryx* published by other writers between 1862 and the end of the 19th century was there any reference that we could find to a prediction by Huxley.

Our search was not without fruit in other directions, however. Nearly six years after the British Museum acquired its *Archaeopteryx*, Huxley in February 1868 gave a discourse at the Royal Institution with the title: "On

Plate XX: Two enlargements of the right-wing area of the main slab. Note spots from an underlying dendritic pattern showing faintly through the thin layer of paste in which the feather impressions were forged.

the Animals which are most nearly intermediate between Birds and Reptiles." Here, surely, was an occasion when one might have expected Huxley to make a considerable point of *Archaeopteryx*, but as if he were telling his audience indirectly that *Archaeopteryx* was a fraud, Huxley made no mention of it. Nor did we find Huxley mentioning *Archaeopteryx* in any of the many printed lectures on birds and reptiles we read in his collected essays. The fossil is often said to provide the best evidence that has yet come to light in support of the transitional forms of the Darwinian theory. Darwin is renowned for amassing even the smallest details in favour of his theory, which is why *The Origin of Species* is such a lengthy book. Yet all Darwin could manage to say about *Archaeopteryx* in his last 6th edition of *The Origin of Species* was:

" . . . (a) strange bird, the Archaeopteryx, with a long lizard-like tail, bearing a pair of feathers on each joint, and with wings furnished with two free claws, has been discovered in the oolitic slates of Solenhofen. Hardly any recent discovery tells us more forcibly than this how little we yet know about the former inhabitants of the world." The lack of enthusiasm for *Archaeopteryx* shown by both Huxley and Darwin is consistant with their knowing, or very much suspecting, that *Archaeopteryx* was a fraud.

Any suggestion therefore that the fossil was produced fraudulently and overtly by supporters of the Darwinian theory does not hold water. Nor could it possibly do so, because the fossil was acquired for the British Museum by Richard Owen, Darwin's strongest scientific opponent. Owen wrote an anonymous review of *The Origin of Species* about which Darwin complained: "It is extremely malignant, clever, and I fear will be very damaging. . . It requires much study to appreciate all the bitter spite . . . He misquotes some passages, altering words inside inverted commas." If historical accounts are to be believed, Owen was extremely anxious to acquire the 1861 specimen without first seeing it for himself. He encouraged the commitment of the Museum's free money over almost a two-year period, at one stage in the purchase of *Archaeopteryx* offering to meet the second year's payment to Karl Häberlein out of his own pocket. This makes no sense at all if Owen thought the fossil to be genuine, for he would then have been adding support to the Darwinian theory. Owen's behaviour only makes sense if he was laying a trap.

Huxley had said of Owen: "... I am as grateful towards (him) as it is possible to be towards a man with whom I feel it necessary to be always on my guard."

"There is a great stir in the scientific world at present about who is to occupy Konig's place at the British Museum, and whether the whole establishment had better not ... be remodelled under Owen's superintendance. The heart-burning and jealousies about this matter are beyond all conception. Owen is both feared and hated ..."

"It is astonishing with what an intense feeling of hatred Owen is regarded by the majority of his contemporaries ... A striking example of (his tricks) is to be found in his article in the last *Quarterly*, where he pillories poor Quekett — a most inoffensive man and his own subordinate — in a manner not more remarkable for its severity than for its bad taste."

All this was still in 1851. Also in 1851 we have Huxley's early opinion of Owen's ability and powers of judgement: "Owen is an able man, but to my mind not so great as he thinks himself. He can only work in the concrete from bone to bone, in abstract reasoning he becomes lost ..." And from 1861, just the time when *Archaeopteryx* was bowing itself onto the world's stage:

"Owen occupied an entirely untenable position. . .

The fact is he made a prodigious blunder in commencing this attack, and now his only chance is to be silent and let people forget the exposure. I do not believe in the whole history of science there is a case of any man of reputation getting himself into such a contemptible position."

These background quotations are all from the easily accessible *Life and Letters of Thomas Henry Huxley* (ed. Leonard Huxley, Macmillan 1903). By 1860 Huxley had long since fallen out with Owen, and it was no surprise that he and Owen should have been on opposite sides of the famous debate at the 1860 meeting of the British Association. On Thursday, 28 June, there was a preliminary session in which Owen delivered an attack on the Darwinian theory, beginning by saying that he "wished to approach the subject in the spirit of a philosopher. (It was) his conviction that there were facts by which the public could come to some conclusion with regard to the probabilities of the truth of Mr Darwin's theory." After these opening remarks, delivered in keeping with an earlier remark of Huxley: "He is so frightfully polite that I never feel thoroughly at home with him", Owen went on to state that "the brain of the gorilla, as compared with the brain of man, differed more than it did when compared with the brain of the very lowest and most problematical of the Quadrumana." *Plus ça change, plus c'est la même chose.* We ourselves have encountered just such a situation many times, of a statement being made with total assurance by a supposed expert in front of a general audience, a statement so wide of the truth that the only effective response one can really make to it is to call the man a liar straight out. Huxley protested as best he could, but it was not until sometime later that Owen got his comeuppance on this matter, from the anatomist W. H. Flowers at the Cambridge meeting in 1862 of the Association, at almost exactly the time Owen, as Superintendant of the Museum's Natural History Section, was negotiating for the purchase of *Archaeopteryx*.

The "great debate" between Huxley and Bishop Wilberforce took place two days after Owen's foray on the gorilla brain, on Saturday, June 30, 1860. Actually it was not a debate at all, for Huxley was not billed to speak. It was a meeting at which Wilberforce, advised in advance by Owen, delivered an attack on Darwin and Huxley: "He ridiculed Darwin badly and Huxley savagely, but all in such dulcet tones, so persuasive a manner, and in such well-turned periods, that I who had been inclined to blame the President for allowing a discussion that could serve no scientific purpose, now forgave him from the bottom of my heart," wrote one witness to the scene.

Huxley said in after years that he had not even intended to go to the meeting, which after the gorilla fiasco of two days earlier would be understandable — there is a limit to the amount of nonsense that can be tolerated. It was only a chance meeting with Robert Chambers which changed his mind. Chambers was not a supporter of Darwin but he was an evolutionist who had been the first to propose that reptiles evolved from fish. He asked Huxley "not to desert them", meaning the evolutionary camp.

The statements one usually reads of the course of the meeting are in some degree inventions, for there was no full contemporary account. The scene as it was set is known however. The Lecture Room of the Oxford Museum was crowded with some 700 persons, long before the protagonists appeared, swinging from the chandeliers as one might say. The clergy, who were to roar mightily for Wilberforce held the middle ground. The raffish undergraduates who were to bang the desks for Huxley were pushed into one of the upper corners. When at last the actors arrived, Professor Henslow took the chair at centre. On his right sat Bishop Wilberforce. To

Wilberforce's right was an American, Dr Draper, who was to begin the meeting, in the lead-off spot as they say in baseball, with the pertinent question: "Are we a fortuitous concourse of atoms?" To the left of Henslow was a clergyman and to the left of the clergyman were Sir Joseph Hooker and Sir John Lubbock. Scenes just like it will be familiar to the modern academic. Although Huxley was to be a target he apparently had no platform seat. The meeting became famous because of Wilberforce's rhetorical question to Huxley, asked as an aside on the spur of the moment: "Was it on his grandfather's or his grandmother's side that he was descended from a monkey?"

This made it inevitable that Huxley would have to speak. Accounts of what he said in response to Wilberforce's question are mostly embroidered, for as Huxley remarked in later years he couldn't remember himself. The reply was delivered instinctively and impromptu. He thought it went something as follows, at the end of his reply: "Lastly, as to the descent from a monkey, I should feel it no shame to have risen from such an origin; but I should feel it a shame to have sprung from one who prostituted the gifts of culture and eloquence to the service of prejudice and falsehood."

That Huxley's reply made a deep impression is certain, for of this there is contemporary evidence: "Mr Huxley slowly and deliberately arose. A slight tall figure, stern and pale, very quiet and very grave, he stood before us and spoke those tremendous words — words which no one seems sure of now, nor, I think, could remember just after they were spoken, for their meaning took our breath away . . . One lady fainted and had to be carried out; I, for one, jumped out of my seat."

Wilberforce almost surely had the best of the knowing smiles and applause. Hooker and Lubbock also spoke for evolution, so that in spite of Wilberforce having the majority, the more thoughtful of the audience (as with the writer above) left having gained the impression that those "most competent to judge the arguments of Darwin saw their way to accepting his conclusions."

Two things stand out clearly with respect to *Archaeopteryx*. The issue of the authenticity or otherwise of the fossil must have been small beer, taken in relation to the social forces that were let loose over the years from 1860 to 1863. The second is that Richard Owen, a 'malignant' opponent of the Darwinian camp, was not remotely going to take trouble, even offering a considerable sum of money out of his own pocket, to secure a genuine fossil that would provide the best possible support for his enemies. The only hypothesis consistent with all the facts and with the psychological forces of the time is that *Archaeopteryx* was acquired as a known fraud, with the intent of trapping Darwin and Huxley into claiming it in support of the evolutionary theory, the fraud being executed in collusion betwen the anti-evolutionary camp in Britain and the experienced forgers of Pappenheim. Every aspect of the situation then fits. Otherwise nothing fits. We understand why Owen bought the fossil unseen, despite rumblings from Germany. Wendt says that "many naturalists denounced the Solnhofen bird as a fraud", and we understand from friends with a feeling for the subtleties of the German language that the well-known paleontologist, Andreas Wagner, expressed delicately worded misgivings concerning the probity of Karl Häberlein, in which case it would have been quite irresponsible for Owen to purchase the fossil unseen, unless of course very different issues were at stake. We understand also why the fossil contained evidence of fraud, the discrepancy between slab and counterslab at the upper left wing area of the slab.

This was to permit the fraud to be 'discovered', once Huxley and Darwin had laid claim to its scientific importance, thereby putting them in an untenable position, when all fossil evidence for evolution could be discounted and derided by the anti-evolutionists.

By the circumstances of the late 20th century, with instant media penetration into anything that can be whipped into a public scandal, it might seem strange that *Archaeopteryx* could have been commissioned as a deliberately executed fraud. But there was no such instant public exposure in 1860. London and Pappenheim were distant places under different jurisdictions. Provided the personalities of those involved met the case, there was nothing to stop such a plan from being hatched. It is abundantly clear from all published records that the Häberleins, father and son, were acutely money-conscious. Provided the price was right the job would be done, and the price paid by the Museum, even though high by the standards of the day, may well have been only a portion of the amount that was really paid. There would in any case always be someone in the Pappenheim area whom Karl Häberlein could blame for the deception, and as for Owen, he could be said to have bought the fossil on trust, even offering his own money in part payment for it. All that needed to be done was to gain a little respectability for the fossil ahead of it being shipped to London. This was done through Hermann von Meyer, the same von Meyer who had been used to validate the fraudulent single feather of Plate II. By means of letters which he received, Andreas Wagner was led to give a description of the fossil to the Academy in Münich (*Müncher Akad. der Wiss.*, 1861, page 146). Häberlein's apparently curious conduct in permitting visiters to glance briefly at the fossil, but not to examine it in detail or to sketch it, now becomes intelligible. By keeping the fossil in the news as it were, a background against which *Archaeopteryx* could be sent to London was established. After it was shipped there was a feeling in Germany that Häberlein had been too hasty in securing a foreign buyer, instead of waiting a little longer for a local purchaser to emerge. The reason for the haste is also clear now. Häberlein did not want a fraud to be on display too close to home.

If, in spite of the above evidence and arguments, one wanted to defend Owen, it could be said that over many years he had been interested in fossil birds and had written a good deal on the subject. To acquire an amazing new fossil from Germany, even at what was then vast expense, might therefore have seemed a natural motivation. Owen might also be said to have been driven to bolster the creationist position, by claiming normal birds to have existed even as far back in the geological record as the Jurassic. It could be argued, moreover, that the mistakes in his 1863 paper (*Transactions of the Royal Society*) were all in this direction and were made with this motivation in mind, as quite likely they were. Yet the reptilian features of *Archaeopteryx* were really obvious and Owen's plan, if this were his plan, deceived very few. Owen must have been aware of Andreas Wagner's paper of 1861 to the Münich Academy of Sciences, in which Wagner named the fossil *Griphosaurus*, 'Enigmatic Reptile', a precisely accurate name, superior to *Archaeopteryx*. Owen had every reason to take notice of Wagner, who besides being one of the foremost paleontologists of his day was, like Owen himself, anti-Darwinian. It was Andreas Wagner who discovered and named *Compsognathus*, and so the close resemblance to *Archaeopteryx* must have been very apparent to him. His scepticism shows already in the title of his paper:

"On a new Fossil Reptile *supposed* (our italics) to be furnished with Feathers."

The scepticism shows still more decisively in the actual text of the paper:

> "The most remarkable thing about it was that a well-marked coat of feathers was present both on the anterior limbs and on the tail. These feathers agreed in their configuration so exactly with those of true birds, that their interpretation as such could hardly be doubted. The discovery of feathers in the lithographic slate was of itself something un-precedented, but their mode of union with the skeleton bordered on the incredible. Thus the tail-feathers were attached to a tail possessing not the least resemblance to that of a bird . . . And the attachment of the wings was still more astonishing; for these, on both the anterior limbs, formed a fan radiating from the extremity of the forearm.
> *Obstrupui, steteruntque comae!* . . . Whether I regarded this mongrel creature as a bird with the tail of a reptile, or as a reptile with bird's feathers, was no matter; the one was as incomprehensible to me as the other."

It is another odd aspect of this whole story that Andreas Wagner died shortly afterwards, before he had the opportunity to examine *Archaeopteryx* in detail, died unexpectedly we have read, although whether the un-expected nature of Wagner's death was part of the story we cannot say. At all events it is clear that Wagner's scepticism to the point of ridicule makes for essentially insuperable difficulty in attempting to write an apologia for Owen. In our interpretation of the situation, Owen's risk was minimal, and his potential gain was enormous by the terms of his own state of mind. To a man whom even in 1851 Huxley had felt he could not trust, a man who contrived to get himself hated to an astonishing degree, a man who could pillory poor Quekett his own subordinate, who anonymously changed words inside inverted commas, who was so charged with emotion as to maintain that the brain of a gorilla differs more from man than it does from the most problematical of the Quadrumana, the matter of a little touching up to a fossil would seem no more than a minor affair.

The only flaw in the plan was what to do if Huxley did not fall into the trap. But to a man who had raised the gorilla question, an issue he was certain to lose in the long run, just to gain a momentary advantage, a man of whom Huxley said: "I do not believe that in the whole history of science there is a case of (anyone) of reputation getting himself into such a . . . position," flaws probably did not seem very relevant. Although we did not succeed in our library search in turning up the reference we sought, there was ample evidence of Huxley speculating that birds evolved from dinosaurs, and it is entirely likely that in his lectures he may have sketched on the blackboard his concept of a transitional bird, to be noted down by members of his audience. So there seems little doubt that Huxley really was expecting a creature like *Archaeopteryx* to appear genuinely in the fossil record. So why, when Owen provided just what he expected, did Huxley not fall into the trap?

Although an examination of the main slab alone might have aroused suspicions, evident proof of forgery turns in all cases on the relation of the main slab to the counter-slab. So we can now appreciate to the full why there is no drawing of the counterslab in the Plates to Owen's paper of 1862, the one in the *Transactions of the Royal Society*. We also understand why we have not come on early photographs or on a cast of the counterslab. Without having either accurate drawings or photographs, or alternatively having the fossil in one's possession for a while, it would be difficult to feel certain a forgery had been committed. It therefore seems rather doubtful that Huxley could have felt absolute certainty on the matter. Rather would his doubts be of Owen, the man against whom he had resolved as early as 1851 to be "always on my guard." Huxley's early journal notes that in January 1841 he began projects in German, Italian, Physiology, Algebra, Geometry, Natural Philosophy, Chemistry, Greek, Latin, English History, Ancient History and English Grammar. The entry for June 20, 1841 admits, however, that so far as Italian, Greek and Latin were concerned nothing had been done. So Huxley may never have read the famous line in Virgil: *Quidquid id est, timeo Danaos et dona ferentes*. But if he hadn't he would surely have been able to invent it. In an age when fossil forgery was not a particularly uncommon phenomenon, the association of *Archaeopteryx* with Owen must have been sufficient to arouse suspicions of fraud.

So the position became one of stalemate, with the Museum simply continuing to house the forgery. Somewhere between 1863 and 1895 the first of the adjustments to the fossil were made, with the upper left wing area of the main slab being then adjusted to fit the counterslab. We do not know whether this was done during Owen's term as Director of the Natural History Section of the Museum or after he had retired in 1884. Nor do we know if the adjustment was done inhouse or if external help was called in. It is an interesting thought that possibly expert forgers from Pappenheim were used. The year 1879 falls mid-way between 1863 and 1895, and this is close to the time of appearance of the 1877 *Archaeopteryx* specimen. If the adjustments were done near 1879 then they were done well within Owen's time at the Museum and under his direction.

The hypothesis that the fossil might have been fixed

with external aid, or even taken for the purpose outside the Museum altogether, cleared up a difficulty we had felt for some time with feather impressions in the upper left wing area of the main slab. While on the one hand we felt that feather impressions would not have been added inhouse by the Museum itself, the evidence pointed to impressions in this area as being something of a patched-up job, done *in situ* without forgers having a clean run at the fossil, as they had in the beginning. The use of a paste of some kind, a filler material, is very obvious when the direction and angle of incidence of the light is right, as in Plate VII. The feather barbs are coarser here, there are fewer of them per unit length than elsewhere on the fossil, and it is in the upper left wing area of the main slab where the subsequent peeling away of feather-bearing material is worst, where the fossil shows the mysterious 'edges' due to some kind of applied layers that we saw in Plate XVI.

So by 1880 or thereabouts the position must have seemed reasonably secure. Nothing had come out, and the fossil itself had been adjusted so that its more obviously fraudulent features were now hidden. The prestigious Berlin Museum had added its imprimatur to *Archaeopteryx*, whether through naivety or otherwise we do not know. To Richard Owen on his retirement in 1884, *Archaeopteryx* must therefore have seemed a dead issue both literally and figuratively, hopefully destined only for a quiet future in some not too prominent a position among the possessions of the Museum. But it was not to be. Owing to the rise to fame of the very theory Owen had sought so desperately to discredit, *Archaeopteryx* was destined to occupy an ever-expanding and more prominent role. Ironically, Owen's fraudulent creation was to acquire the fame he had longed-for so ardently himself.

CHAPTER 6

Archaeopteryx – More on the Origin of Birds

It is not often that one has the opportunity to write a book that seems destined to be offensive to everybody. Scientists who for a lifetime have accepted *Archaeopteryx* as the lynch pin of their beliefs will not be pleased of course. Nor is our unfortunate tendency to fall into a derisive style likely to be seen as very pleasant either, especially when one of the targets of our remarks is to be reckoned among the most massive pillars of the Establishment. At one stage we received a suggestion by telephone that a panel of four distinguished sedimentary geologists be appointed, two by the Museum, two by us, to pronounce on the authenticity of the fossil. Our reply was typical of all that is objectionable in our way of expressing things. It was that if a panel of distinguished sedimentologists could not see that it is impossible to dig-out tens of thousands of feather barbs to within an accuracy of a fifth of a millimetre by assaulting a face of rock then god help sedimentary geology. Besides which, controversies are not settled in the quantitative sciences in such a ludicrous way.

We might in all this have expected to win the plaudits of anti-evolutionists, 'creationists' as they are known nowadays. Downing *Archaeopteryx*, with the resulting cut at the Darwinian theory, might be expected to receive loud applause on this other side of the fence. But no, for instead of *Archaeopteryx* turning out to be a Darwinian fraud, it was just the opposite. *Archaeopteryx* was a creationist fraud.

With the persistent accuracy of reporting that is our worst handicap, it has to be admitted that we entered into this whole affair also with the thought of taking a cut at the Darwinian theory, but regrettably perhaps that was not the way the investigation turned out. Nor had we remotely expected Thomas Henry Huxley to turn out the hero of the drama. Our early forays into the biological history of the 19th century had left us with a negative impression of Huxley, because previously we had been concerned with the Darwin-Wallace priority question on which we felt Huxley had been ungenerous towards Wallace. It became clear, however, in our more recent readings why this had happened. To Huxley, the core of the matter lay in the struggle against conformist opinion, a struggle over the existence of evolution, a polemical struggle in which Wallace took no part and was glad to avoid, although Wallace in 1855 had shown more than any other contemporary biologist that evolution really had taken place. Wallace's interest was in why and how evolution had occurred. When in 1870 Wallace arrived at the conclusion that an influence from outside the terrestrial ensemble of plants and animals was needed, there seemed to Huxley to be something more than a whiff of creationism. On all this we remain of our original persuasion, for the pursuit of the truth is of more ultimate importance than a struggle against conformist opinion, although we readily admit that the downing of wrong conformist opinion is often a practical neccessity for progress. Even so, we have always felt that if people, including scientists, want to think wrongly on an issue then it is their privilege to do so. To take a different view is to take a road that inevitably leads to intolerance, in our opinion.

With this said, we were not prepared for Thomas Henry Huxley to emerge in his own writings as a totally different character from anything we had read about him in the writings of others. Instead of a stiff, unyielding, combative person we found, especially in the more personal letters, a wit and bubbling sense of humour that proved something very different. As we followed Huxley from the flash of youth in which he set himself projects in Italian, German, Physiology, Geometry. . . to the considerable fortitude with which he bore developing arthritis and advancing deafness in his later years, a sympathetic character, very human as one says, had emerged. What also emerged was a scientific perception, hitherto overlooked, which had it been followed, together with Wallace's perception of 1870, would have anticipated the genetic storms discussed in Chapter 1.

Huxley wrote to Darwin on 23 November 1859, immediately after reading *The Origin of Species*, which had just then been published, a letter that contains a tremendous paragraph:

"The only objections that have occurred to me are — 1st, that you have loaded yourself with an unnecessary difficulty in adopting: *Natura non facit saltum* so unreservedly; and 2nd, it is not clear to me why, if continual physical conditions are of so little moment as you suppose, variation should occur at all."

Here was Huxley at the very threshold of the need for the concept of a genetic storm.

The reader may well wonder what Darwin really did that was new. Patrick Matthew has coined the words 'natural selection' as early as 1831, and had discussed the importance of natural selection in a correct way, albeit publishing his ideas in an odd place and written in a rather harum-scarum style (*Naval Timber and Arboriculture,* Longman, London and Edinburgh MDCCCXXXI). The same ideas were extended and published in 1835 by Edward Blyth in a leading journal of the day ("Varieties of Animals" in *The Magazine of Natural History*). In the 1840's Robert Chambers suggested that reptiles had evolved from fish, and a decade or so later Huxley suggested that birds had evolved from reptiles, and Wallace in 1858 gave, we think with clear priority, the hitherto missing concept of what became called the principle of divergence. So what did Darwin contribute? *Natura non facit saltum,* nature does not go in jumps, which is just what nature actually does, it goes in genetic storms. The only wrong idea in the whole ensemble was Darwin's. It was his only idea, and Huxley even warned him against it in the letter of November 1859. The reason why Darwin emerged in later decades as an apparently great scientific figure lay in the ferocious polemic which followed the publication of *The Origin of Species,* a book which is simply a compendium of the ideas detailed above. The polemic forced the ideas to be fused together into one point of view to which the name Darwinism became attached. But Darwinism was the work of many men, with Wallace, who actually coined the name, outstanding. Wallace had no taste for polemics. He was a brilliant writer who expressed in only a few pages all that is of real scientific value in *The Origin of Species.* Yet one cannot see Wallace rising 'stern and pale' and delivering the 'tremendous words' which caused a lady to faint and to be carried out supine from the 1860 Oxford meeting of the British Association.

Back to *Archaeopteryx!* When Richard Owen retired in 1884 the British Museum had a lemon in its cupboards. The best advice to be given to Owen's successors would have been to squeeze out the lemon, to have done with it once and for all. But it need not surprise us that a different view was taken, say nothing and hope the thing would go away. It is a matter of experience in our own times that people in establishment posts are not given to rocking the boat unless they feel badly frustrated in their ambitions. Life was harder economically in the late 19th century, so the situation in this respect was then accentuated. Besides which, there is a selective factor of an almost biological kind whereby people with the temperament to have gotten the *Archaeopteryx* affair settled and done with once and for all are not to be found in establishment posts. Such people exist in appreciable number, but as self-employed persons facing the world on their own merits, or if they are particularly able or fortunate, running larger businesses of one kind and another.

The excuses to be made in such situations are legion, not to offend poor old Owen now that he is retired, not to make fools out of colleagues in Berlin — international connections usually provide match-winning arguments in the establishment, and likely enough those who followed Owen in authority at the Museum felt themselves compromised by earlier events. Vide poor Quekett, Owen probably took care to make sure that his subordinates were sufficiently compromised to make certain of their silence. So the thing went on and on, with *Archaeopteryx* continuing to swing in the cupboard, an innocent little dinosaur come back 160 million years later to haunt the world.

As the years continued there came an ironic turnaround. *Archaeopteryx* became accepted as an important demonstration of the correctness of Darwinism, now the current orthodox doctrine. No longer need the Museum have any conscience about it, for what could possibly be wrong with supporting what all right-thinking persons believed to be the truth? What was wrong of course is that the truth does not need supporting by false arguments and deceit. The truth will stand on its own merits. So the Darwinian theory was lumbered by a fraud which both Huxley and Darwin had themselves rejected. Down the years, the *Archaeopteryx* establishment grew and grew, given impetus by de Beer's book of 1954, which achieves an apparent scholarly quality through devoting itself mainly to a description of the genuine dinosaur around which the fraudulent aspects of *Archaeopteryx* were constructed.

In reading through the literature on *Archaeopteryx* that has appeared over the past century it is interesting to observe how those who have come nearest to the truth have been the most reviled. In a paper, "An Analysis of the Characters of *Archaeopterix* and *Archaeornis*. Were they Reptiles or Birds?" (*Ibis*, volume 86, 1944, page 517) P. R. Lowe came very near the truth:

". . . I have tried to analyse as many parts and characters as were available in the make-up and fossil-imprints of *Archaeornis* (the specimen of 1877) and *Archaeopteryx* (the British Museum specimen) with the object of determining, if I could, whether they were reptilian or avian. To my surprise, with the exception of the feathers, I could find no characters that were definitely avian as opposed to reptilian."

Lowe did not manage to conceive that he was dealing with a fraud, and so he decided the discrepant feathers must have been used for gliding, an error he would hardly have fallen into if hang-gliding had been a popular sport in 1944, for then the advantage of a winged membrane over weakly attached feathers must have forced him to the correct final conclusion. Nevertheless, Lowe decided that *Archaeopteryx* could not have been the forerunner of birds and must be dismissed as simply a reptilian aberration, which had been our own position before the intervention of Lee Spetner.

From the point of view of the *Archaeopteryx* establishment, Lowe was outside the pale, as one can see from the magisterial manner in which the error-prone de Beer seeks to dispose of him. When heretics turn out to be right they are seldom given proper credit by scientific establishments, the denigation continues unchecked. Even J. H. Ostrom, the most accurate of the establishment in our opinion, could not forebear writing in his article *Origin of Birds* (*loc. cit*):

"A much better-known view, which has received considerable criticism, is that of Lowe, who assessed the (bone structure) of *Archaeopteryx* and *Archaeornis* as non-avian and almost completely reptilian. On those grounds, he concluded that these creatures were not birds but feathered dinosaurs! — and too specialized to have given rise to true birds. As I will try to show later, Lowe was essentially correct in his assessment of the skeletal evidence, but he failed to recognize how ideally intermediate many of those structures were between reptilian and avian conditions." In other words, although Lowe was right he was wrong, because reptiles were half-birds already.

The present position of the *Archaeopteryx* establishment is that the 1861 and 1877 specimens were creatures indistinguishable from dinosaurs except for feathers, feathers modern in form with the wonderful properties that permit modern birds to perform both amazing aerobatics and long-distance flight over the whole Earth, but which *Archaeopteryx* could not have used for any flight worth speaking about because of inadequate attachments and inadequate muscular power. One can judge this story laughable, outrageous or merely pathetic according as one sees it.

We have not come out of this investigation with an excessively high opinion of the commonsense displayed by paleontologists. Paleontology suffers in our opinion from the ease with which persons of strong character can impress views on their colleagues, views based either on fraud or vestigial evidence, views which then become repeated endlessly in the literature and imposed on students in the classroom. Again in our opinion, persons of strong character who claim to discover in the fossil record just what the scientific consensus of the day expects are to be looked at with something a little more than a raised eyebrow. Experience in other parts of science shows that the scientific consensus rarely succeeds in anticipating exactly the way the world turns out to be. Even with the advantage of being able to observe other planets with the aid of Earth-based telescopes over many generations astronomers did not anticipate in anything like the proper richness of detail what any one of the distant planets has turned-out to be like. It has been known since the time of Cassini (1625-1712) that Saturn possesses a divided ring system, but nobody over a quarter of a millennium guessed that Saturn's ring would be divided into the astonishing multiplicity which the Voyager missions recently revealed. Men simply cannot guess ahead of time the full richness of the way things really are, and claims to have done so are automatically to be viewed with suspicion.

Such a person as we have in mind was Othniel C. Marsh, of whom Wendt wrote, thinking in praise but actually in condemnation, that nobody had exceeded Marsh in the ability to fill gaps in the fossil record. Of this there is excellent documentary evidence in *The Life and Letters of Thomas Henry Huxley* (Volume 2, page 202 to 212). To precis the story, Huxley visited the United States in 1876, spending a week with Marsh at Yale

College, New Haven, beginning the 9th of August. Huxley was to give a major lecture in New York and he was anxious to hear what Marsh had to say on the evolution of horses:

"At each enquiry (as to) whether he (Marsh) had a specimen to illustrate such and such a point or exemplify a transition from earlier and less specialised forms to later and more specialised ones, Professor Marsh would simply turn to an assistant and bid him fetch box number so and so, until Huxley turned on him and said, 'I believe you are a magician; whatever I want, you just conjure it up.' "

As a consequence of what he had heard from Marsh, Huxley changed the content of the lecture in New York and also of subsequent lectures in Philadelphia. On the occasion of the latter, Huxley remarked:

"Thus, thanks to these important researches (Marsh's), it has become evident that, so far as our present knowledge extends, the history of the horse-type is exactly and precisely that which could have been predicted from a knowledge of the principles of evolution. And the knowledge we now possess justifies us completely in the anticipation that when the still lower Eocene deposits, and those which belong to the Cretaceous epoch, have yielded up their remains of ancestral equine animals, we shall find, first, a form with four complete toes . . ., while, in still older forms . . . we (shall) come to the five-toed animals, in which, if the doctrine of evolution is well-founded, the whole series must have taken its origin."

Huxley's biographer, his son Leonard, then continues:

"Seldom has prophecy been sooner fulfilled. Within two months, Professor Marsh had discovered a new genus of equine mammals, Eohippus, from the lowest Eocene deposits of the West, which corresponds very nearly to the description given above."

Othniel C. Marsh it was who also discovered *Icthyornis* and *Hesperornis* that we met in Chapter 1, which are said to be birds from the Cretaceous period, before the genetic storm which brought about the massive extinctions at the Cretaceous-Tertiary boundary. These discoveries, following not long after *Archaeopteryx*, led to a situation in which, according to Wendt:

"Evolutionists burst into cheers at the discovery of these . . . birds. For now it could be posited that in the Cretaceous there had probably been a large number of different descendants of the *Archaeopteryx*. The gap between modern birds and the most primitive of birds seemed to be closing, thanks to Marsh's discoveries."

Our last quotation is from *Organic Evolution* by R. S. Lull (Macmillan, New York 1949) who states:

"Two original mounted skeletons of *Hesperornis* and two of *Ichthyornis*, the latter unique, are preserved at Yale."

There are two unique feathered specimens of *Archaeopteryx* and two unique specimens of *Icthyornis*. Although we understand *Icthyornis* has no literal feather impressions, there is a sense in which it and *Archaeopteryx* can be said to be birds of the same feather.

In spite of the frauds and fakes to which paleontology rather naturally lends itself, we think the broad picture given by the fossil record is probably substantially correct, thanks to the great majority of paleontologists being fully earnest in their search for the truth, with only occasional distortions introduced by men of overweening ambition. As time goes on, distortions become isolated in the record and can eventually be removed by the lack of general confirmation.

What emerges in the record seems to us most remarkable. It is the contrast between clearly evolving forms like the mammals and largely non-evolving forms like many orders of invertebrates — insects, spiders, scorpions, shrimps. Some of the latter can be traced back without much change in the record for great spans of time, in some cases even to the Cambrian, close to the Precambrian boundary, which is defined in geology as the time, about 570 million years ago, when multicelled life first became common on the Earth. The evolving forms become lost, however, in time intervals far shorter than this, lost in the case of the mammals about 65 million years ago at the Cretaceous-Tertiary boundary, as we saw in Chapter 1.

We do not think the evolutionary lines are lost because of gross imperfections in the fossil record, the usual defence offered by supporters of 'Darwinism'. Viewed against the vast sweep of modern geology, which goes back in time almost 4,000 million years, the Cretaceous-Tertiary boundary is really very recent. There is a multitude of rock sequences dating within the last 100 million years, open for inspection up and down the world, and there is nowadays almost an army of geologists available to do the inspection. So the explanation for the failure to trace evolving lines backward beyond a certain stage requires a different explanation. It is that evolution has largely proceeded by genetic storms. The paleontologist can 'see through' the smaller storms to what occurred before them, but a vast storm like the one at the Cretaceous-Tertiary boundary produced such enormous changes in all species subject to viral invasion that it is hard to match what appeared after the storm to what was present before the storm. The paleontologist looks for fragmentary anatomical connections, the shape of a particular bone or the form of a particular tooth, but what would be an adequate guide if evolution proceeded slowly in tiny steps is not adequate through a big genetic storm, for the reason that there are many alternatives for connecting the later forms to the earlier ones.

This is not to say joining up what happened after with what was present before is impossible, but that it is difficult. It is not strictly impossible to reverse a so-called irreversible process in physical chemistry, but doing so in practice is difficult to the point of impossibility. The world is full of processes that are comparatively easy to argue one way but extremely difficult to argue the opposite way. A cloud of gas condenses to form a star and the problem, although not altogether easy, is within the range one can consider manageable. But try to go from a star to the cloud of gas that formed it and the problem is truly unmanageable. To this day the sun must contain a memory of the cloud of gas from which our solar system formed, but even if we could identify that memory the calculation backward in time would be grossly beyond our capacity.

The reason lies in what the Cambridge mathematician J. E. Littlewood once called the 'hook and slice' effect, not in golf but in the property of differential equations. Suppose you know the correct equations for turning back the solar system to the cloud from which it formed, and suppose you possess a very powerful and fast computer. In the nature of things you cannot have perfect precision and it is necessary to decide to what accuracy you will work. Suppose you decide on ten decimal accuracy in the recording of numbers. That is to say you accept a lack of precision in the eleventh decimal place, and then set your calculation going. As you work backward in time you then find your errors begin to escalate. What started as an error in the eleventh decimal place of your numbers becomes an error in the tenth place, then an error in the ninth place, and so on, worse and worse. So you stop the calculation and decide to begin again with twenty decimal accuracy. The calculation goes better for a while, you manage to go a bit further back in time. But then just the same thing happens. So now, thoroughly mad at the cussedness of things, you decide to give it a real go by working to a hundred decimal accuracy. The calculation holds up now for quite a while, so that you think you have the trouble licked. But no, sooner or later it begins again, just the way it was before. Likewise for a thousand decimal accuracy or a million decimal accuracy. The solution is there but you can't find it by practical calculation.

Hopefully the problem for paleontologists is not as difficult as a physical irreversible process, but the situation has something of the same quality about it. Given various animals subject to viral invasion, it is much less difficult to argue forwards as to what they might become than argue backwards from presentday forms to what they were before. Whenever a major grafting occurs in a genetic storm the difficulty presents itself. When we say the mammals originated in a major genetic storm at the Cretaceous-Tertiary boundary we do not mean that nothing was present before. There had to be something in order that grafting was possible. We mean that finding what the previous form or forms were is difficult and perhaps even intractable. Similarly for birds. Reptilian ancestors to birds from before the Cretaceous-Tertiary boundary must certainly have existed, but what they were we do not know. What they were *not* we do know. They were not *Archaeopteryx* or *Icthyornis*.

The next time a spotted flycatcher makes its way from Africa to within two yards of your front door, or a crow called Hitchcock goes clean off its rocker and terrorises the valley, you will therefore know only very partially what you are dealing with, a transformed dinosaur of high quality, but with a remote ancestory that is as obscure as our own.

Index

A

Al-Mufti, S., 43.
Apatornis, 32.
Archaeornis, 124, 125.
Attenborough, David, 39, 44, 58, 59, 71, 103, 104.

B

Baptornis, 32.
Barlow, F. O., 83, 85.
Berlin Museum, 8, 41, 90, 97, 118, 119.
Berlin specimen of *Archaeopteryx,* 44, 66, 89, 90, 97.
Bird flight compared with airplanes, 14, 15.
Bones of Archaeopteryx, 87ff.
Brain case of *Archaeopteryx,* 98ff.
British Association of the Advancement of Science meeting on 28 June 1860, 109, 122.
British Journal of Photography, 47, 48, 99.
British Museum, 8, 44, 46, 48, 66, 76, 77, 79, 83, 85, 87, 89, 90, 91, 93, 95, 97, 99, 100, 105, 108, 117, 118, 119, 122, 123, 124.

C

Cardiff Museum, 77.
Chambers, Robert, 110, 122.
Charig, Dr. A. J., 46, 89, 97, 98.
Compsognathus, 7, 32, 33, 51, 55, 60, 61, 66, 67, 70, 72, 74, 77, 87, 90, 91, 98, 114.
Cottingham, E. T., 50.
Cratchett, Bob, 94.
Crawley, Geoffrey, 47, 99.
Cretateous birds, 32.
Cretateous-Tertiary boundary,
    extinctions, 28, 29, 31, 128, 131
    origin of birds, 35, 131.
Crow, 15-17.

D

Darwin, C., 39, 40, 103-5, 107, 109, 110, 112, 113, 120-122, 124.
Darwin, C. and *Archaeopteryx,* 107.
Darwinian theory of evolution through natural selection, 19, 20, 22, 101, 103, 108, 109, 119, 120, 122, 129.
de Beer, G., 32, 46, 47, 61, 66, 67, 70, 83, 87, 89, 91, 93-95.
Dendrites, 91.
Dendritic patterns, 100, 101, 102, 106.
Dinosaurs, extinction of, 28.